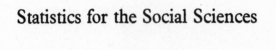

Statistics for the Social Sciences

An Introduction to

Statistics

for the

Social Sciences

SECOND EDITION
ENLARGED

By

T. G. CONNOLLY

B.Sc., Ph.D.
*Principal, West Ham College
of Further Education*

and

W. SLUCKIN

B.Sc. Eng., B.Sc., Ph.D.Lond.
*Lecturer in Psychology
University of Leicester*

MACMILLAN
London · Melbourne · Toronto
ST MARTIN'S PRESS
New York
1969

© *T. G. Connolly & W. Sluckin* 1962

First Edition 1953
Second Edition 1957
Reprinted 1962, 1969

Published by
MACMILLAN AND CO LTD
Little Essex Street London W C 2
and also at Bombay Calcutta and Madras
Macmillan South Africa (Publishers) Pty Ltd Johannesburg
The Macmillan Company of Australia Pty Ltd Melbourne
The Macmillan Company of Canada Ltd Toronto
St Martin's Press Inc New York
Gill and Macmillan Ltd Dublin

Printed in Great Britain by
JARROLD AND SONS LTD NORWICH

Preface to Second Edition

The attempt made by the first edition of this book to help students of social sciences, psychology, education and cognate subjects who find Statistics somewhat baffling, was accorded a pleasant measure of appreciation; and in this new edition, the authors, besides somewhat improving and expanding the text here and there, have introduced a chapter on the Elementary Analysis of Variance, a technique nowadays not out of place in a first book of Statistics. The book is written for those students who have to satisfy examiners in Statistics and also need for their studies a degree of statistical insight, yet have no knowledge of Mathematics beyond simple Arithmetic. They will find that it is not difficult to acquire the necessary facility in handling experimental data, and above all, to obtain a clear understanding of the nature of basic statistical procedures. Perhaps what prevents many students from coming to grips with Statistics is that they have not really expected to encounter mathematics after leaving school. The book has evidently had some success in enabling arts and social studies students to overcome their initial difficulties, and in giving a good basis for more advanced work. The scope of the book is that of a General B.A. or B.Sc. Degree; it covers the Social Science and Social Studies degree courses in most British Universities; and it provides the basic needs of Psychology Honours students. The stress is not on any special techniques such as are used by economists, sociologists or psychologists, but on sound knowledge of the foundations of the subject.

The present reprint incorporates a number of minor amendments and corrections.

November 1962

T.G.C.
W.S.

Contents

vii

CHAPTER I

The Frequency Distribution

The word "statistics" is used in three distinct senses:
(1) *Statistics* may mean a collection of numerical data.
In this sense the term is commonly used in everyday life.
(2) *Statistics* may refer primarily to methods of elucidation
of quantitative data (the data being generally affected by
a multiplicity of causes). This is the sense in which the
term is used in the title of this and similar books.
(3) *Statistics* may be the plural of *a statistic*. The meaning of
this term is fully explained later in connection with sampling theory. Broadly, in this sense statistics are characteristic measures of samples.

Measurement and Statistics. Where measurements are
reproducible, there may be no need for statistical methods. In
some of the physical sciences, that which is being studied can
often be measured and its true magnitude readily established.
Under controlled experimental conditions the influence of each
of the factors upon what is being measured may be examined
one at a time. However, in research and in industrial experimentation many factors affecting a process may be beyond
control or may be unknown; or the measurements themselves
may involve an element of error. It is then that measurements are not reproducible.

In various fields, for example in agriculture or even in
chemistry, experimentation cannot usually approach the ideal
of varying one thing at a time. In a field like meteorology
observation and not experimentation is the rule. Each event
is a result of numerous causes, and observational data must be
treated statistically if useful information is to be extracted.

The social sciences, too, almost invariably yield quantitative
data which can only be analysed statistically. If objective and
reliable information is to be had, quantification of observa-

tional results is necessary. Observation of this kind constitutes measurement, though measurement which is not fully reproducible and which is subject to error. Data based on such measurement must be collected, suitably arranged and analysed in various ways before being adjudged; in a word, such data must be submitted to a statistical treatment. We shall see step by step, from the simple to the more complex, how statistical treatment of data is carried out.

Unordered Data. The economist, sociologist, educationist, or psychologist, having finished his field work in the investigation of a problem, usually finds himself confronted with a mass of unordered data. This information has usually little meaning or significance until it has been organised and classified in a systematic way.

Thus we are at first confronted with a set of individual measurements taken as they come. They may be, say, yields of wheat in bushels per acre obtained by a number of farmers, or, perhaps, the so-called Intelligence Quotients (I.Q.s) of some students or army recruits, or some other data of this kind. For the sake of example consider Table I which sets out I.Q.s of a group of fifty men. A glance at the table gives merely a vague general conception of how the scores run numerically but nothing more.

TABLE I

THE TABULATION OF I.Q.S OF FIFTY MEN

97	110	105	96	109	95	108	117	107	110
(L) 82	99	93	116	(H)126	125	108	90	118	116
124	114	101	112	120	113	110	101	103	115
107	102	123	106	105	106	120	100	107	119
120	112	92	103	86	104	97	101	109	105

H Highest value.   L Lowest value.

Now the investigator usually wants to know several things concerning such data. He wants to know, for example, what is the I.Q. of the average or typical man. He wants to know something about the variability of intelligence in the group, that is how big are the differences between individuals. He may wish to know something about the scatter of the students, i.e. whether they tend to bunch up towards the higher or lower scores, or towards the middle, or whether they are more or less equally scattered throughout the range. In order to begin answering this sort of questions about a set of measurements such as that in Table I, the measurements must first be organised into what is known as a *frequency distribution*.

Grouping into Class Intervals. The first task in such an organisation of our material is to group the measures or scores into classes or categories. Clear thinking about large numbers of facts necessitates condensation and organisation of the data in a systematic form. We are forced to group our data into classes, and the statistical treatment of the data depends to some extent upon the determination of these classes.

The procedure of classifying begins with the calculation of the *range*. This is found by subtracting the lowest measure from the highest. In Table I it is shown that the lowest I.Q. is 82, and the highest is 126; thus the range is 126–82 or 44.

The next thing that has to be decided is the number of class intervals and the size of each interval. The choice here will be determined by two general principles of statistical practice that have arisen out of much experience.

First the number of class intervals must be not less than 10 or more than 20, and the general tendency is to restrict the boundaries to between 10 and 15 intervals. A small number of groups is favoured partly because frequently there is a small number of individual measurements in the sample and partly because a small number of groups is much more convenient to handle. Grouping, however, introduces minor errors into the calculations, and the smaller the number of groups, the larger these errors tend to be. Thus accuracy of calculation favours a larger number of classes. These two points of view must be borne in mind when deciding in any particular case upon the number of classes to be used. In all cases, however, the number should conform to the rule given above.

The second guiding principle is that certain sizes of class-interval are to be preferred, the preferred ones being 1, 2, 3, 5, 10 and 20. Almost all data can be easily handled by being grouped into classes that contain any one of these ranges of measures.

Let us now apply these principles to our data from Table I. We have already calculated the range to be 44. The "distance" from the lowest measurement to the highest is, in terms of I.Q. units, 44. This range must now be divided into a number of equal intervals.

The number of classes which this range will give is found by dividing the range by the size of the interval chosen, "and adding one". Thus choosing an interval of 3 units, 44 divided by 3 gives 14, to which 1 is added, giving 15 as the number of classes. This number of classes satisfies the first rule. If an interval of 2 units had been chosen it would have yielded 22 plus 1, or 23 classes, which is too large a number. An interval of 5 will yield 10 classes, and this also satisfies our guiding rule. What size of interval shall we choose then, 3 or 5? Our sample contains 50 cases, which is a relatively small number for statistical work, so we may choose the interval of 5 which gives us the minimum number of groups, i.e. 10.

Calculating the Frequencies. We are now in a position to tabulate the separate measures within their proper class intervals. This has been done in Table II. In the first column of this table the class intervals have been listed, placing the lowest measures at the bottom of the table and the highest at the top according to accepted custom. Each class interval comprises exactly 5 measures. Thus the first interval 80–84 should be read as "80 up to 84". That is, it contains all measures of 80, 81, 82, 83 and 84. The second interval begins with 85 and ends with 89, thus including 85, 86, 87, 88 and 89. The bottom and top measures are what we call the *limits of the interval*. They do not indicate exactly where each interval begins and ends. We shall be concerned later in this chapter with the *exact limits* of the intervals, but these *score limits*—as they are often called—are useful in tallying and labelling the intervals.

Each measure in Table I is now taken as it comes, and placed in its proper interval in Column 2 of Table II by placing a tally mark in the row for that interval. It will be noticed that the tallying is done in groups of five, each fifth tally mark being drawn across the previous four. This is very helpful in totting up the frequencies. When the tallying has been

TABLE II

FREQUENCY DISTRIBUTION OF I.Q.S OF FIFTY MEN

Col. 1 I.Q s	Col. 2 Tally Marks	Col. 3 Frequencies f
125–129	||	2
120–124	++++	5
115–119	++++ |	6
110–114	++++ ||	7
105–109	++++ ++++ ||	12
100–104	++++ |||	8
95–99	++++	5
90–94	|||	3
85–89	|	1
80–84	|	1

$$\Sigma f = N = 50$$

completed the tally marks in each row are added up to find the frequency (f), or total number of cases that fall within each interval. These frequencies are entered in Column 3 of the table.

The next step is to check the tallying. The frequencies in Column 3 are summed and the total placed at the bottom of the column. The Greek Σ, capital sigma, means the "sum of", and Σf means "the sum of the frequencies". If the work has been done accurately and the tallying has neither omitted nor duplicated any of the measurements, then Σf should equal N, that is, the total number of individual measures in our sample. If Σf does not equal N, the tallying must be done again until it does check.

Even when the tallying does check there is another possible source of error. One or more tally marks may have been placed in the wrong interval. The only way to check this sort of error would be to repeat the tallying process, a very tedious piece of work when dealing with, say, three or four hundred cases. Care should, therefore, be taken to make the calculation of the frequencies correct at the first attempt.

Exact Limits of Class Intervals. It will be noticed that in Table II, although the lowest I.Q. is 82 the lowest interval begins at 80. We could have started the lowest interval with the lowest score, yielding intervals of 82–86, 87–91, and so on. It is much more convenient, however, and it facilitates tabulation and later calculations, if we start the intervals with their lowest score at multiples of the size of the interval. This holds for any interval size used. If the interval is 3, start class intervals at 12, 15, 18, etc.; when the interval is 10, start them at 40, 50, 60, etc. In this way the lowest measure will be "contained in" and will not necessarily be at the beginning of the first interval.

It was mentioned earlier that the score limits were not the exact limits. We shall find, however, that in statistical calculations it is essential to think in terms of exact limits. Consider the first interval 80–84. This—we said—contained the measures or scores of 80, 81, 82, 83 and 84. A measure of 80, however, means in effect anything from 79·5 to 80·5; a measure of 82 means 81·5 to 82·5; of 84, 83·5 to 84·5, and so on. Thus an interval of 80–84 has exact limits of 79·5 to 84·5. This principle holds no matter what the size of the interval, or where it begins. An interval labelled 24 to 26 includes scores or measures 24, 25 and 26 and extends exactly from 23·5 to 26·5. An interval labelled 80–89 has exact limits of 79·5 and 89·5. It will be seen that by following this principle each interval begins exactly where the one below it ends, which is as it should be. There is no need to be confused by this. The intervals with their exact limits should read "79·5 up to 84·5", which means it includes 84, 84·1, 84·2, 84·3, 84·4, but not 84·5. The next interval contains 84·5, 84·6, etc., "up to", but not including 89·5. Table III shows as an illustration the exact limits of the intervals alongside the score limits, which we have chosen in our tabulation.

When is one to tabulate the score limits and when the exact limits? It is certainly more convenient to put down 80–84

TABLE III

CLASS INTERVALS AND THEIR MID-POINTS FROM THE
DISTRIBUTION OF THE I.Q. DATA

Score Limits	Exact Limits	Mid-points	f
125–129	124·5–129·5	127	2
120–124	119·5–124·5	122	5
115–119	114·5–119·5	117	6
110–114	109·5–114·5	112	7
105–109	104·5–109·5	107	12
100–104	99·5–104·5	102	8
95–99	94·5–99·5	97	5
90–94	89·5–94·5	92	3
85–89	84·5–89·5	87	1
80–84	79·5–84·5	82	1

than 79·5–84·5. Provided always that one constantly remembers that the "expressed" limits are not the "exact" limits, that for instance, 80–84 begins at 79·5 and ends at 84·5, then the intervals may be tabulated as they have been in Table II.

A comparison of Table I and Table II will now show the value of the frequency distribution. In Table II the organised data are more meaningful and we get a more complete picture of the group as a whole. We see, for example, that the most frequent I.Q.s fall in the interval of 105–109, and that the others tend to group themselves about this interval. The average must fall somewhere between 100 and 114. At either end of the range the frequencies fall off, relatively low and high I.Q.s being rare. The greatest bunching comes just past the middle of the range and in the upper half. Useful indeed as this tabulation is, much better pictures of the distribution can be got by presenting the data in graphical forms.

Graphic Representations of Frequency Distributions.
The fundamental aim of all statistical organisation of data is to
secure a clear picture and interpretation of the situation
represented by the data. Classifying the data into the frequency distribution in the manner outlined above is the first
step in this direction. It will be shown in the next two chapters
that there are two major numerical methods of further
condensing the material. Each of these methods condenses the
whole of the data into a number; and these two numbers, one a
measure of "central tendency", the other a measure of
"variability or dispersion", are of considerable importance in
the description and interpretation of the facts.

Before concerning ourselves with these numerical conden-
sations, however, we must first consider the two standard
graphical methods of presenting the facts of the frequency
distribution. Such graphic presentation helps to interpret the
statistical data. Certainly it seeks to translate numerical
information, sometimes difficult to grasp or comprehend, into
pictorial form which is, perhaps, more concrete and more
readily understandable. Thus, graphic presentation gives a
better picture of a frequency distribution, setting out its
general contour and showing more concisely the number of
cases in each interval.

The two standard methods of graphically representing a
frequency distribution yield the *frequency polygon* and the
histogram. These two will be discussed here. Two further
methods, yielding the *cumulative frequency graph* and the
cumulative percentage curve, will be treated in a later
chapter.

How to Plot a Frequency Polygon. The data of Table I,
represented in the form of a frequency polygon, are shown in
Fig. 1. The word polygon means many-sided figure, and a
glance at Fig. 1 will indicate the aptness of the term.

The figure is drawn on graph paper. In general a convenient
type of paper is the one that is divided into inch squares with
heavy lines, and further subdivided into tenths of an inch with
lighter lines. With regard to the overall size of the figure, the
base line to be easily readable should be at least five or six
inches long; and for the sake of good appearance and to make
easy the reading of the figure, the standard practice is to make
the maximum height of the figure from 75 per cent to 100 per

cent of its total width. Keeping these general points in mind, the steps in making the frequency polygon are as follows:

1. Note the numerical amount of the range and rule a base line of suitable length.

2. Lay off the units of the frequency distribution on the base line, and mark clearly the "exact limits" of the class

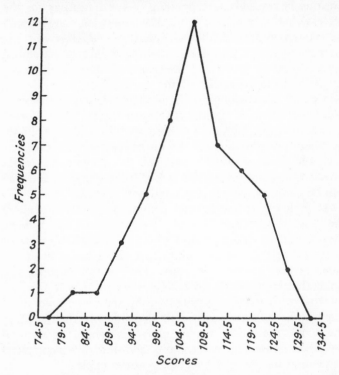

FIG. 1. A FREQUENCY POLYGON PLOTTED FROM THE DISTRIBUTION
OF THE I.Q.s IN TABLE I

intervals. In the present example we have been dealing with class intervals of 5 units, and we have a total of 10 intervals to each of which corresponds a frequency value. In drawing the diagram, however, we must always allow for two extra intervals, one at each end, in order to enable the diagram to be brought down to the base line, as shown in Fig. 1. Our base line here is divided up into 12 equally spaced intervals, beginning with 74·5 and ending with 134·5.

3. At the left-hand end of the base line erect a vertical axis, and mark off on this axis successive units to represent the frequencies. As mentioned above, the height of the diagram should be no greater than its width.

4. At the mid-point of each interval (see Table III) on the base line, go up in the direction of the vertical axis until a position is reached corresponding to the frequency for that interval, and here place a point. It is important that this point be plotted exactly at the mid-point of the interval. The assumption here is that all the scores in an interval are equally spaced over the whole of it; therefore, the logical choice of a single value to represent all the scores in an interval is its mid-point. This assumption is not always strictly justifiable; it holds best when the number of scores is large and the intervals are not too wide. But, even if these conditions do not hold, the mid-point assumption does not introduce a serious error, and generally about as many scores will fall above as below the various mid-point values, and lack of balance in some intervals will be offset by the opposite condition in others.

A simple rule to find the mid-point values is to average either the "exact" or "score" limits. For example in our problem the interval containing scores 95 to 99 inclusive has exact limits of 94·5 to 99·5. Subtracting these limits gives the range of the interval as 5 units. Half of this range is 2·5. Going thus far above the lower limit, the mid-point is 94·5 plus 2·5, that is 97 exactly. Similarly using the score limits of 95 and 99, the difference is 4, half the difference is 2, and 95 plus 2 gives the mid-point value of 97. In Table III are set out the score limits, the exact limits and the mid-points, and frequencies for the class intervals in our example.

5. In the interval next below the bottom one and next above the top one there are no scores, thus the frequency to be recorded at the mid-point of these intervals is zero, and the points are thus placed on the base line.

6. The points are joined with straight lines to give the frequency polygon.

How to Plot a Histogram. The second standard method of graphically portraying a frequency distribution is by means of a histogram. This type of graph, sometimes also called a column diagram, is illustrated in Fig. 2. Most points applying to the plotting of frequency polygons apply also to the plotting of histograms. In fact the procedure in setting out is identical with one exception; there is no need to include the two extra intervals one below the bottom one and one above the top. Now although the points representing the frequencies are located as before at the mid-points of the intervals, these points are not joined by ruled lines. Instead, a horizontal line is ruled through each point extending it to the "exact limits" of

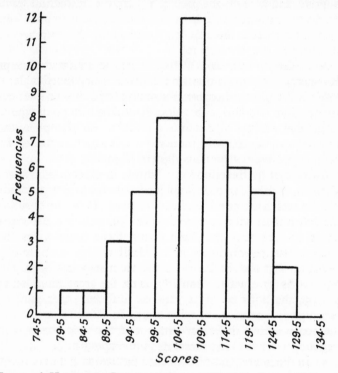

FIG. 2. A HISTOGRAM PLOTTED FROM THE DISTRIBUTION OF I.Q.s IN TABLE I

each interval, and vertical lines are then drawn from the exact limits on the base line to complete the rectangles or columns.

Both the frequency polygon and the histogram tell the same story. Both are useful in enabling us to see in graphic form how the scores are distributed, whether symmetrically or whether piled up at the low or the high end. On the whole the frequency polygon is preferred for a number of reasons. First it certainly gives a clearer conception of the contour or shape of the distribution. Whereas the histogram gives a stepwise change from one interval to the next, based on the assumption that the cases in each interval are evenly distributed, the polygon gives the more correct impression that the cases in each interval are grouped towards the side nearer the greater frequency. It must be admitted however that the histogram is more exact than the polygon. In the histogram each measurement occupies exactly the same amount of area, and each rectangle is directly proportional to the number of measures within that interval.

A further advantage of the frequency polygon, and perhaps the most important, is that frequently it is necessary to compare two frequency distributions on the same base line. If the distributions overlap, as they usually do, the histogram type of graph would give a very confused picture. An example of the clear comparison of two frequency distributions afforded by the polygon type of graph is illustrated in Fig. 3.

Comparing Distribution Shapes. A new question arises when we wish to compare graphically two frequency distributions in which the number of cases differs. If the difference is large then there may be considerable difficulty in plotting the two graphs on the same base line. If the polygon for the smaller distribution is made sufficiently large to be easily readable, that for the larger distribution may not fit on the sheet. Conversely if the distribution for the greater number of cases is made to be of reasonable size, the other may be ridiculously small.

Comparison of different distributions is very common in statistical work, and in general it is the shapes, the positions on the base lines and the dispersions that we wish to compare. Apart then from any difficulty in plotting, a marked difference in size would make such comparisons very difficult and unsatisfactory. To obviate these difficulties the usual practice is to plot the *percentage* of cases rather than the *number* of cases for each class interval.

To illustrate the procedure of transforming frequencies into percentages, Table IV gives the distributions of scores on a "trade test" made by two groups of army trainees. N_1, the number of cases in the first group, is 70, whereas N_2, the number of cases in the second, is 180. When, however, the frequencies have been converted into percentage frequencies P_1 and P_2, the position is as if we had two distributions, each having $N = 100$.

TABLE IV

PERCENTAGE FREQUENCY DISTRIBUTIONS OF "TRADE TEST" SCORES FOR TWO GROUPS OF ARMY TRAINEES

Trade Test Scores	Mid-points	f_1	f_2	P_1	P_2
80–89	84·5	0	10	0	5·6
70–79	74·5	6	16	8·6	8·8
60–69	64·5	12	36	17·1	20·0
50–59	54·5	18	52	25·7	28·9
40–49	44·5	13	31	18·5	17·2
30–39	34·5	10	22	14·3	12·2
20–29	24·5	7	13	10·0	7·2
10–19	14·5	4	0	5·7	0

$$N_1 = 70 \quad N_2 = 180$$

To convert a frequency into a percentage all that is required is to divide the frequency by N and multiply by 100. For example, Table IV indicates that in the first group, scores of 50–59 were achieved by 18 individuals. The total number in this group was 70, so to convert the frequency of 18 into a percentage, 18 is divided by 70, and the result multiplied by 100, yielding 25·7. A shorter method, particularly useful when using calculating machines or slide-rules, is to calculate the quotient $\dfrac{100}{N}$, and then multiply each frequency in turn by this ratio.

In Fig. 3 the frequency polygons representing the two distributions have been plotted on the same base using percentage frequencies instead of the original f-values. These polygons provide an immediate comparison of the two groups;

such a comparison would not have been possible if the graphs had been plotted from the original frequencies. The better achievement of the second group is evident, as also is its greater average. Over the whole range the second group has a small but definite advantage. The scatter or dispersion factors—a matter which will be dealt with in detail later—appear to be about the same. Over the whole range the comparison of frequencies interval by interval is readily available.

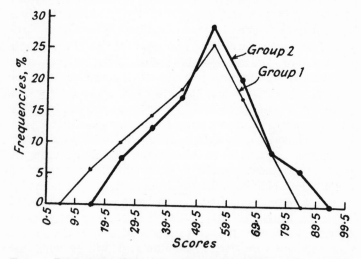

FIG. 3. PERCENTAGE FREQUENCY DISTRIBUTIONS OF "TRADE TEST" SCORES FROM THE DATA IN TABLE IV

Smoothing a Frequency Polygon. In dealing with the data of Table I, it was not explicitly stated whether the fifty men constituted the whole body of men in question, or were merely a "sample". If the fifty were the whole lot, then they would be known statistically as a "population". If on the other hand the fifty men are simply a group selected from a much larger body of men, then the group is known statistically as a "sample of the population". By far the greatest amount of statistical work is the handling of data from samples of populations, and the major purpose of the work is invariably to study the population through the medium of the sample. By the statistical treatment of a properly selected sample of measures, it is possible to estimate with varying degrees of confidence, how the particular variable quality will be distributed in the population at large.

The whole theory of sampling is from a beginner's point of view quite involved; it is extremely important and will be dealt with at some length later. However, for the moment suppose that our fifty men do constitute a properly selected sample of a larger population, say for example, of a large class of army recruits. We wish to forecast from the representative sample how the larger population will distribute itself. Now a glance at the frequency polygon of Fig. 1 shows that it is somewhat irregular and jagged in outline. What sort of curve would we have got if we had increased the size of the sample to, say, 100? On the assumption that the larger population has practically the same properties as those exhibited by the sample, we should expect that gradually increasing the size of the sample would yield curves that are successively smoother and less subject to chance irregularities.

To get a notion of how the figure might look if we had taken information from all the population, and not just a sample, we predict from the frequencies we have, what the corresponding frequencies would be in the larger population. The method is known as *smoothing* the frequency polygon, and is illustrated in Table V. In this table the observed frequencies are given in Column 3 and the expected or predicted frequencies for the total population are given in Column 4. It will be noted that two class intervals have been added at the ends of the range of scores.

The smoothing consists of taking a series of "running" averages from which the expected frequencies are calculated. To find a "smoothed" f for a particular interval, add together the f-values for that interval, and the f-values for the two adjacent intervals, and divide by 3 to get the average. Thus the observed frequency for the interval 105–109 is 12; for the interval above, 110–114, it is 7, and for the interval 100–104 below, it is 8. The predicted frequency for the interval 105–109 is then $(12 + 7 + 8) \div 3$, or 9·00. The smoothed frequencies for the other intervals are calculated in the same way; the values are set out in Table V.

Note the procedure necessary to calculate the smoothed f-values for the extremes of the range, that is for the top and

TABLE V

ORIGINAL AND SMOOTHED FREQUENCIES FOR DISTRIBUTION
OF I.Q.s FROM TABLE I

Col. 1 Scores	Col. 2 Mid-points	Col. 3 Original Frequencies f_o	Col. 4 Smoothed Frequencies f_e
130–134	132	0	0·67
125–129	127	2	2·33
120–124	122	5	4·33
115–119	117	6	6·00
110–114	112	7	8·33
105–109	107	12	9·00
100–104	102	8	8·33
95–99	97	5	5·33
90–94	92	3	3·00
85–89	87	1	1·67
80–84	82	1	0·67
75–79	77	0	0·33

$N = 49·99$

bottom intervals, 75–79 and 130–134. Here there are no
f-values above the top one or below the bottom one, so that
we must use in each case a frequency of 0. Thus the predicted
frequency for the interval 75–79 is (0 + 0 + 1) ÷ 3, or 0·33,
and for the interval 130–134 it is (0 + 0 + 2) ÷ 3, or 0·67.

The smoothed polygon is shown in Fig. 4, superposed on
the original one. It is always important to show the original
data when presenting a smoothed polygon so that the reader
will see what the observed facts were. We can expect with
some confidence that the larger population from which the
sample was drawn will distribute itself more like the smoother

curve than the original one—that is, if our sampling was statistically sound.

To what extent can this smoothing process be carried? It is very doubtful whether a second smoothing is ever warranted. The larger the size of the sample, the smoother, in fact, will be

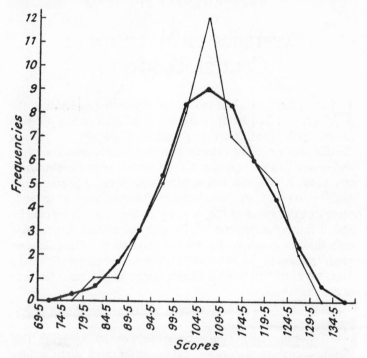

FIG. 4. SMOOTHED POLYGON FOR THE I.Q. DISTRIBUTION, SUPER-POSED ON ORIGINAL POLYGON

the original polygon. This in effect means that the larger the initial sample, the more the original figure will approximate that of the distribution of the whole population. The best advice that can be given to the beginner in statistics is to take large samples, to smooth as little as possible, and, whenever reasonable, to present the original data alongside the adjusted result.

CHAPTER II

Averages or Measures of Central Tendency

Having dealt with the method of organising material in the form of a frequency distribution, we are now in a position to take up the consideration of methods of statistically treating the distribution. The organisation of data into class intervals, and hence into a frequency distribution, is only a preliminary step towards a definite quantitative treatment. The frequency distribution with its graphic representations may adequately represent the status of the data, but it does not enable concise and definite comparison of the features of one distribution with those of another. In order to make such comparisons we need "measures" of the condensation and organisation of the data; we need "numerical descriptions" of the basic features of the distribution.

There are three principle types of numerical description of frequency distributions.

1. A measure of *central tendency* or an average: this measure enables a concise statement of how distributions differ in "position", as shown by the size of the measure around which the others largely cluster.

2. A measure of *variability*: this indicates the way in which the separate measures of two distributions "scatter" or "fluctuate" around the average.

3. A measure of relationship or *correlation*: this is a numerical method of defining the degree of relationship that exists, if any, between the measures of one distribution and those of another. It enables us to answer such questions as what is the relationship between, say, height and weight, age and intelligence, income and size of family, poverty and delinquency, etc.

In the present chapter we shall be concerned with measures

18

of central tendency or averages of which there are several kinds. Three of these, the *arithmetic mean*, the *median* and the *mode*, are in common use, while two others, the *geometric mean* and the *harmonic mean*, have a more restricted use. In statistical work, however, the term "average" is used generally to cover any measure of central tendency.

Two important purposes are served by a measure of central tendency. First it is a concise, brief and economical "description" of a mass of data. It is a simple measure that represents all the measures in a sample, and as mentioned above, it enables us to compare two or more distributions. Secondly it describes indirectly, but with some accuracy, the population from which the sample was drawn.

This is important: we rarely or never know the average of a population, and it is only because the average of a sample is a close estimate of the average of a population that we can generalise and make predictions beyond the limits of the sample. This makes possible scientific investigation in the social sciences. Now if we rarely or never know population averages, how can we tell how closely our sample averages approximate them? Provided our sampling has been done correctly, it will be shown later that there are methods of calculating the degree of confidence we can have in our sample averages as representing population averages. For the present, however, let us concern ourselves with the methods for calculating the various averages.

The Arithmetic Mean: The Mean of Ungrouped Data. In its most commonly used form, the word average refers to the arithmetic mean. To calculate it, all that is necessary is to add up all the measurements and divide by the number of measurements. The formula for such a calculation is

$$M = (\Sigma X)/N$$

where M is the arithmetic mean
Σ—"the sum of"
X—an individual measure
N—the number of measurements.

For example, if the price of a certain commodity in five different localities is £3, £3 10s., £3 5s., £3 2s. and £3 3s., then the average or mean price (£3 4s.) is calculated by adding all the prices and dividing by the number of prices.

The Arithmetic Mean of Grouped Data. When the measures have been grouped into a frequency distribution, the calculation of the mean is slightly different. The formula we use this time is

$$(\Sigma fX)/N$$

where *M* and Σ have the same denotation as before,
   X is the midpoint of a class interval, and
   f is the number of cases in an interval.

The method is illustrated in Table VI.

TABLE VI

AGE DISTRIBUTION OF FEMALE WORKERS IN A TEXTILE MILL

Col. 1 Age Group	Col. 2 Mid-point	Col. 3 f	Col. 4 fX
60–64	62	2	124
55–59	57	2	114
50–54	52	6	312
45–49	47	8	376
40–44	42	12	504
35–39	37	14	518
30–34	32	24	768
25–29	27	12	324
20–24	22	16	352
15–19	17	4	68
		$N = 100$	$\Sigma fX = 3460$

$$M = (\Sigma fX)/N = 3460/100 = 34 \cdot 6 \text{ yrs.}$$

This method assumes that the mid-point value represents all the measures in the interval. For example the table shows that there were 12 individuals in the age group 40–44. Instead of concerning ourselves with the exact ages, we treat them as if the twelve were all 42 years old, 42 being the value of the mid-point for the interval. This is not a strictly true representation of all cases. However the error in any specific case will be small, and in the actual calculation of the mean most of the small errors will tend to cancel each other out, making the final result essentially correct.

As each measure is now represented by the mid-point value, we must multiply the mid-point value by the number of cases in the interval. This means finding for each interval the product of f times X or fX. This has been done in Column 4. The sum of the fX values came to 3460, and the total number of cases N being 100, the mean is found by dividing the 3460 by 100, and is equal to 34·6. If we had put down all the ages in a long column, added them up, and divided by 100, we should have got the same result with probably a minor discrepancy.

The Short Method for Calculating the Mean. Frequently in statistical work the measurements are large, and if the frequencies and mid-point values are also large, the method above involves a lot of tedious calculation. To obviate this there is a quick short-cut method that makes the actual calculation much simpler. Further, as will be shown in the next chapter, this short-cut method involves a considerable saving in time and work when calculating a measure of variability known as the standard deviation. The method is illustrated in Table VII; the same data as in the previous example are used.

As the method is a very important one in statistical calculations the reader will be instructed in the use of it step by step.

1. Look at the first three columns of the table and make a reasonable guess as to which interval contains the mean. A common procedure is to take the interval with the greatest frequency. In Column 3 the greatest frequency is 24, but the greater total of frequencies above 24 indicates that the mean will be possibly higher so we may choose the interval with a frequency of 14, that is age group 35–39. It is most important to appreciate that this method will give exactly the same result, no matter which interval we start with. The more reasonable our guess, however, the simpler will be the calculation. Our guessed or assumed mean, or A.M., is then the mid-point of this interval, i.e. 37.

2. In Column 4 this interval is given the value 0. The first interval above is given the value +1, the second +2, the third

TABLE VII

AGE DISTRIBUTION OF FEMALE WORKERS IN A TEXTILE MILL

Col. 1		Col. 2	Col. 3	Col. 4	Col. 5
Age Group		Mid-point X	f	x'	fx'
	60–64	62	2	+5	+10
	55–59	57	2	+4	+8
	50–54	52	6	+3	+18
	45–49	47	8	+2	+16
	40–44	42	12	+1	+12 +64
A.M.	35–39	37	14	0	
	30–34	32	24	−1	−24
	25–29	27	12	−2	−24
	20–24	22	16	−3	−48
	15–19	17	4	−4	−16 −112
Totals			$N = 100$		$\Sigma fx' = -48$

$$i = 5$$
$$c' = (\Sigma fx')/N$$
$$c = ic' = i[(\Sigma fx')/N] = 5 \times (-48/100)$$
$$= -240/100 = -2\cdot40$$
$$M = A.M. + c = 37 - 2\cdot40 = 34\cdot6 \text{ yrs.}$$

+3, and so on. The first interval below is given the value −1, the next −2, and so on. These are the deviations (x') of the mid-points of the different intervals from the A.M. in units of class interval. Thus 62, the mid-point of the interval 60–64, is 5 class intervals above the A.M. In like manner 22, the mid-point of interval 20–24, is 3 intervals below the A.M., that is, it is −3 class intervals away from the A.M.

3. These deviations are multiplied by the frequencies, interval by interval, and the products are entered in Column 5

headed fx'. It is important to take great care that the algebraic signs are correct.

4. Sum the fx' values in Column 5 algebraically. This has been done in two steps. The sum of the positive products is $+64$, and the sum of the negative ones is -112. The algebraic sum of the whole column $(\Sigma fx')$ is then $64 - 112$, or -48.

5. Divide this sum of the fx' products by N, the sum of the frequencies or total number of cases in the sample. This can be expressed in mathematical terms as $c' = (\Sigma fx')/N$; it is the correction factor in class interval units.

6. In order to calculate the correction c that must be applied to our guessed mean to arrive at the true mean, the quotient above is multiplied by the size of an interval i, that is the number of units in an interval. Thus,

$$c = c'i = i[(\Sigma fx')/N] = 5 \times (-48/100) = -240/100 = -2\cdot40,$$

which is the correction factor in terms of measurements or scores.

7. This correction is added algebraically to the guessed mean, and the result is the true mean. Thus

$$M = A.M. + c = 37 - 2\cdot4 = 34\cdot6 \text{ yrs.}$$

It will be noticed that the result is identically the same as that achieved by the earlier method, but the actual calculation involved is much simplified.

The Median is the second type of statistical average which we shall consider. The median is the mid-point of the series. It is the point on the measuring scale above which fall exactly one half the cases and below which fall the other half.

The Median of Ungrouped Data. Two situations arise in calculating the median from ungrouped data, one when N is even and one when N is odd. Suppose we have the following numbers of men absent from work at a factory on eleven successive working days: 18, 16, 14, 24, 13, 8, 11, 18, 18, 19, 14. If we arrange these numbers in order of size, we have

8, 11, 13, 14, 14, (16), 18, 18, 18, 19, 24;

then 16 is the median, since 16 is the mid-point or the measure that lies midway in the series. There are five measures above and five measures below 16, and, as 16 is the mid-point of a range from $15\cdot5$ to $16\cdot5$, then 16 is the median.

If now we drop out the first number 8, our series is then

11, 13, 14, 14, 16, 18, 18, 18, 19, 24,

and contains ten items. The median is the point in the series above which lie five cases and below which lie the other five. The first five cases take us up to and include the 16. A measure of 16, however, means anything from 15·5 to 16·5, so that our counting really takes us up to the upper limit of 16, or 16·5. The upper half extends down to the first 18 and as this represents a range of 17·5–18·5 our counting takes us down to 17·5, the lower limit. The median then lies half-way between 16·5 and 17·5, and is the average of the two, or 17·0.

The Median of Grouped Data. When the data are grouped, the calculation of the median follows the method illustrated in Table VIII.

TABLE VIII

CALCULATION OF MEDIAN OF AGE DISTRIBUTION OF FEMALE WORKERS IN A TEXTILE MILL

Age Group	f	
60–64	2	
55–59	2	
50–54	6	
45–49	8	
40–44	12	
35–39	14	44 cases down to here
30–34	24	Median interval
25–29	12	32 cases up to here
20–24	16	
15–19	4	

Median (a) 29·5 + (18/24)5 = 33·25 yrs.
       (b) 34·5 − (6/24)5 = 33·25 yrs.

Here, as before, the task is to determine the point on the scale on either side of which lie half the cases. As the total number of cases in this example is 100, then 50 will lie on either side of the median. Our problem is how to locate such a value in a frequency distribution in which the identities of the individual items have been lost.

Starting at the bottom of the frequency column, the frequencies are added up until the interval which contains the 50th case from the bottom is reached. This interval is called the "median interval". In the table the median interval is the interval 30–34. Thirty-two cases took us up to the "top" of interval 25–29. The next or median interval contains 24 cases, thus the 50th case lies somewhere in this interval. The problem is to determine where it lies. We assume for the sake of interpolation that the 24 cases in this interval are evenly distributed over the whole range of the interval whose exact limits are 29·5 and 34·5. We need 18 more cases to make up the 50, so we must go 18/24 of the way up into this interval. The total range of the interval is 34·5 − 29·5 or 5, so we go 18/24 of 5 or 3·75 units up into the interval. Adding the 3·75 on to the exact lower limit of the interval which is 29·5, we get the median value of 29·5 + 3·75, which is 33·25.

This can be checked, of course, by working down from the top. Starting at the top of the frequency column, 44 cases take us down to the interval 35–39. We need 6 more cases to make up the 50. We must therefore go 6/24 of the way down into the median interval. As before, the interval range is 5, so we go down 6/24 of 5 or 1·25 units. This we now subtract from the exact upper limit of the median interval which is 34·5. The median value is then 34·5 − 1·25, or 33·25, as before.

The whole procedure can be summed up neatly by expressing it in mathematical symbols

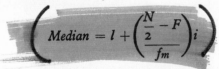

$$Median = l + \left(\frac{\frac{N}{2} - F}{f_m} \right) i$$

where l — lower exact limit of median interval;

$\dfrac{N}{2}$ — one half of the total number of cases;

F — sum of all the frequencies up to, but not including, the median interval;

fm — the frequency within the median interval;

i — size of class interval, found by subtracting the exact limits of an interval.

If N is an odd number the procedure is exactly the same as when it is even. For example if N were 85, then $N/2$ in the formula above would become 42·5, and the median value would be calculated exactly as before.

The Mode. This is the third type of statistical average. It is the value which most frequently appears in the distribution. It is the most "probable" value since it occurs most frequently.

The modal wage for example, is the wage that is earned by more people than any other wage. The modal shoe size is that size which is taken by more individuals than any other size. The modal cost of production of flour is that cost that is characteristic of more flour mills than any other cost. When we have ungrouped data, the mode then is that particular measurement that occurs most frequently or has the maximum frequency.

Calculation of Mode from Grouped Data. When the data are grouped into a frequency distribution we normally distinguish between a "crude" mode and a more accurate "interpolated" mode.

The crude mode is the mid-point of the class interval having the greatest frequency. In Table VIII the modal interval is the interval 30–34 as it has the greatest frequency 24. The crude mode then is the mid-point of this interval, which is 32. Not infrequently a distribution may yield two intervals each with the same maximum frequency. If these two intervals are separated by more than one intervening interval, then we say that the distribution has two modes or is "bimodal". If, however, they are separated by only one intervening interval, it is probable that the distribution is really unimodal, particularly if the intervening interval has itself a relatively high frequency. In such a case there is no way of deciding what is the crude mode. When the two like maximum frequencies occupy adjacent intervals then the reasonable thing is to assign the crude mode to the dividing point between the two intervals.

When the number of cases is not very large, say, when it is less than 100, then it is usual not to go beyond the determination of the crude mode. When distributions are noticeably skewed however, and also when samples are large, the mid-point value is not a sufficiently accurate estimate. We then interpolate within the modal interval to obtain a more accurate estimate. The formula for obtaining the interpolated mode is

$$Mode = l + \left(\frac{d_1}{d_1 + d_2} \right) i$$

where l — lower exact limit of modal interval;

d_1 — difference between the frequency of the modal interval and the frequency of the preceding interval;

d_2 — difference between the frequency of the modal interval and the frequency of the next following interval;

i — size of class interval.

As an illustration of interpolating a modal value let us apply this formula to the data from Table VIII.

35–39	14	
30–34	24	Modal interval
25–29	12	

The modal interval has $f = 24$, the preceding interval has $f = 12$, and the following interval has $f = 14$. The exact lower limit of the modal interval is 29·5 and the length of a class interval is 5. Thus we have the following

$$Mode = 29·5 + \left[\frac{(24 - 12)}{(24 - 12) + (24 - 14)} \right] 5$$

$$= 29·5 + \left[\frac{12}{12 + 10} \right] 5 = 32·2 \text{ yrs.}$$

Notice what has happened. The estimate of the mode has been "pulled away" from the mid-point value towards the following interval. This following interval has a frequency of 14 compared with a lesser frequency of 12 for the interval preceding the modal interval. If the frequency of the preceding interval had been the larger, then the pull would have been towards the lower interval.

Only in very rare instances will the mid-point value be a final estimate of the mode. It should only be used when samples are small. Quite obviously if different intervals had been used, the mid-point of the modal class would have been different. The interpolation improves the estimate of the mode by allowing the adjoining frequencies to add their weight in reaching a final estimate.

When to Use the Mean, Median and Mode. The three averages or measures of central tendency described above are those in most common use in statistical calculations. The problem now is which is to be used in any given circumstance. In order to answer this question let us consider some of the characteristics of each of these three measures.

The arithmetic mean is widely used because it is easily computed and easily understood. In addition, however, it has certain special properties which enhance its use in certain cases.

First it must be noted that all the measures in the distribution contribute their weight to the calculation of the mean. The extremely small values and the extremely large ones, as well as those near the centre of the distribution, influence this average.

A further important property of the mean is that it is generally the most accurate, or reliable, of the three measures of central tendency. Reliability has a special strict meaning in statistical work. We mean here that from sample to sample of the total population, this measure will fluctuate less widely than either of the other two. Errors of measurement tend to neutralise one another around the arithmetic mean, and the error of this average can be shown to be considerably smaller than the error of a single measure.

Finally, the arithmetic mean is better suited to further statistical calculations. It will be shown in later chapters that the short method of computing the mean is an essential step in the determination of two very important statistics, the "standard deviation", and the "correlation coefficient". When distributions are reasonably symmetrical, we may almost always use the mean, and in fact should prefer it to the median and the mode.

The median, as we have seen, is a positional average. To

locate the median we require the serial order of values only, the actual numerical values being important only in so far as they determine the serial order. Thus all the measures contribute to the calculation of the median, but their magnitude is only used indirectly. It is then less affected by the extremes of the distribution than is the arithmetic mean. For example the median of the series 2, 5, 8, 9 and 11, is 8. If the extreme values are changed so that the series is now 6, 7, 8, 15 and 24, the median remains 8, but the arithmetic mean has changed from 7 to 12. The fact that the median is influenced by the number rather than the size of the extremes in the distribution makes it a useful average in some cases.

The mode is typical in that it is the value which characterises more items than any other value. Thus, it is typical of a frequency distribution in a significant way, and is an especially meaningful average in certain problems. For example, the average size of hat worn by the male population of Great Britain would be a useful piece of information to a hat maker. The modal size, however, would be more useful than the mean or median size. More men actually wear the modal sized hat than wear any other size. Further, the mode is probably the quickest estimate of central tendency available.

In general then, when deciding which average to use apply the following rules.

1. Use the arithmetic mean when:
    (a) the greatest reliability is required,
    (b) the distribution is reasonably symmetrical,
    (c) subsequent statistical calculations are to be made

2. Use the median when:
    (a) distributions are badly skewed,
    (b) a quick and easily calculated average is required,
    (c) extreme measures would affect the mean disproportionately.

3. Use the mode when:
    (a) the quickest estimate of central tendency is required,
    (b) the most typical value is required.

The Geometric Mean of two numbers is found by multiplying the two numbers together and finding the square root of the product. Thus the G.M. of 9 and 4 is

$$\sqrt{9 \times 4} = \sqrt{36} = 6$$

The G.M. of three numbers is found by multiplying the three numbers together and finding the cube root of the product. The G.M. of 2, 4, and 8, is

$$\sqrt[3]{2 \times 4 \times 8} = \sqrt[3]{64} = 4$$

The G.M. of n numbers is found by multiplying them together and finding the nth root of the product.

$$\text{G.M.} = \sqrt[n]{X_1 \times X_2 \times X_3 \times \ldots X_n}$$

When a number of measurements are to be averaged in this way, we resort to the use of logarithms, as anything beyond the square and cube roots presents a computational problem. Thus the calculation can be expressed in symbols as follows,

$$\log \text{G.M.} = \Sigma(\log X)/n,$$

and having calculated log G.M., the antilog gives the geometric mean itself.

This average is used in special situations; two of the most important are:

1. certain special cases of averaging ratios, and
2. average rates of change.

Table IX gives an illustration of the use of the geometric mean; the set of data is hypothetical.

Column 2 gives the prices P_1 in 1940; Column 3 gives the prices P_2 in 1950. In Column 4, the later price is expressed as a percentage of the earlier. The problem is to find the average percentage change in food prices. The items in Column 4 are not individual measurements but are ratios, and to average these ratios we use the geometric mean. The log of each ratio is expressed in Column 5. The sum of the logs of the ratios is 23·1077, and dividing this by 10, the number of items, the log of the geometric mean is obtained; it is 2·3108. The value of the antilog of this, the geometric mean, is 204·6, and thus the average increase of food prices is 104·6 per cent.

When rates of increase of population, of performance, of production, of sales, etc., are expressed as ratios or percentages of previous measurements, the correct average to use is the geometric mean. Quite obviously, it is only practically adapted to the solution of short series.

TABLE IX

RELATIVE FOOD COMMODITY PRICES FOR YEARS 1950 AND 1940

Col. 1 Com- modity	Col. 2 P_1 Price 1940	Col. 3 P_2 Price 1950	Col. 4 X P_2 as % of P_1	Col. 5 Log X
Milk	s. d. 3 pt.	s. d. 5½ pt.	% 183·3	2·2632
Eggs	2 0 doz.	4 6 doz.	225·0	2·3522
Tea	2 10 lb.	4 0 lb.	141·2	2·1498
Butter	1 0 lb.	2 0 lb.	200·0	2·3010
Bread	3½ lb.	6 lb.	171·4	2·2340
Bacon	1 7 lb.	3 2 lb.	190·0	2·2788
Meat	6 lb.	1 8 lb.	333·3	2·5288
Sugar	3 lb.	6 lb.	200·0	2·3010
Potatoes	1 lb.	2 lb.	200·0	2·3010
Cheese	8 lb.	1 7 lb.	250·0	2·3979

$N = 10$ $\Sigma \log X = 23\cdot1077$

$$\log \text{G.M.} = 23\cdot1077/10 = 2\cdot3108$$
$$\text{G.M.} = 204\cdot6$$

Average increase per cent in food prices is 104·6.

The Harmonic Mean is the last kind of statistical average we have to deal with; it is used in problems including the averaging of time rates. A rate is a ratio, and as such it may be stated in either of two forms. If there are two measurements A and B, they can be expressed as a ratio as A/B, or B/A. Suppose a time study was being made of production in a factory department. Two measurements would be required: the number of units produced, and the time taken, say, in hours. If these two measurements are indicated by N and T

respectively, then the production rate may be expressed as
"N/T units per hour", or "T/N hours to produce one unit".

Consider the following example. In a time study of five
factory workers assembling radio components, the following
results were recorded.

A. 12 components per hour.   5   minutes per component.
B.   4   „   „   „   15   „   „   „
C. 10   „   „   „   6   „   „   „
D.   8   „   „   „   7·5   „   „   „
E.   6   „   „   „   10   „   „   „

$$5)\overline{40}$$ $$5)\overline{43·5}$$

8   „   „   „   8·7   „   „   „

and therefore, $\dfrac{60}{8} = 7·5$ minutes per component.

The rates have been expressed in two ways, "the number of
units produced per hour", and "the time taken to produce
one unit". The arithmetic mean was calculated for the
individual records in both series, and the average time to
produce one unit was computed. From the first series the
average time to produce one unit was calculated to be 7·5
minutes, while the second series yielded a result of 8·7
minutes. This is a difference of 15 per cent. Why is there a
difference at all?

The answer to this question is that the two series are not
comparable at all until they have been reduced to the same
basis. Suppose that the study were for the purpose of costing
production; then, the basis would be "the fraction of an hour
required to produce one component". This is precisely the
way the second series has been stated. If we wish to answer
our question with the data recorded in its first form, we must
first obtain the reciprocals of the rates. The reciprocal of
a number N is simply $1/N$. Having found the reciprocals, we
then find their arithmetic mean. This, in fact, amounts to
finding the harmonic mean, H.M., of the original numbers. In
order to calculate H.M. the following formula is used:

$$1/\text{H.M.} = 1/N \times [\Sigma(1/X)]$$

where H.M. — harmonic mean,
     N — number of cases,
     X — an individual measurement.

The H.M. of the rates in their first form is calculated as in Table X.

TABLE X

COMPUTATION OF A HARMONIC MEAN OF
PRODUCTION RATES

Person	X No. of Units per Hour	$1/X$ Reciprocals of Rates
A	12	0·0833
B	4	0·2500
C	10	0·1000
D	8	0·1250
E	6	0·1667

$$N = 5 \qquad\qquad \Sigma(1/X) = 0.7250$$
$$1/\text{H.M.} = (1/5)0.7250 = 0.1450$$
$$\text{H.M.} = 1/0.1450 = 6.897 \text{ units per hour}$$
$$60/6.897 = 8.7 \text{ minutes required to produce one unit}$$
"according to the harmonic mean".

The calculation in the table shows that if the H.M. is used instead of the arithmetic mean, then the average number of units produced per hour is 6·897, as against 8 in the first case when the arithmetic mean is used. Further, 6·897 units per hour is equivalent to an average production time of 8·7 minutes per unit. This is exactly what is obtained by finding the arithmetic mean of the rates in the second form. Thus, if the data were recorded in "numbers of units per hour", the harmonic mean would be employed to compute "the average time per unit". Conversely, if the data were recorded as "number of minutes per unit" then the harmonic mean would be required to compute "the average number of units per minute". In general, then, the harmonic mean must be used in averaging time rates only if the recorded rates make variable a factor which it is desired to keep constant.

CHAPTER III

Measures of Variability

A measure of central tendency is the first important characteristic of a frequency distribution. It tells us much about
a distribution but by no means does it give us a complete
picture. When it is necessary to compare two distributions, if
the comparison is made solely on the basis of the averages,
quite wrong conclusions may be drawn. Other statistical
measurements must be used with averages to amplify the
description of a set of data. We shall now consider some
further attributes of frequency distributions which can be
expressed as numbers.

Dispersion and Skewness. Two distributions of statistical data may be symmetrical and may have the same means,
medians and modes. Yet they may differ markedly in the
distribution of the individual values about the measure of
central tendency. Two sample groups of workers from two
different factories may have the same average weekly output
in terms of components assembled; let this be, say, 100 units.
In establishing piece rates it may be concluded that taken as
a whole each group is as productive as the other. If, however, we have the additional information that one group has
no individuals who produce less than 90 or more than 110,
whereas the other has individuals with productive rates
ranging from 65 to 135, we recognise immediately that there
is a decided difference between the two groups in variability
of production. One group is definitely rather homogeneous
with respect to production, the other rather heterogeneous.
A piece rate established for the former group on the basis of
the average production per man may well be a satisfactory one.
For the second group, however, with the same average, the
same rate would, perhaps, place an undue strain on the
laggards at one extreme, while possibly providing an inadequate incentive for the rapid producers at the other end of the

34

distribution. The distributions for two such groups are shown in Fig. 5.

We obviously need a measure of the degree of dispersion so that we may, by referring to a single number, tell whether a frequency distribution is compact or spread out and scattered.

We have already made reference to symmetrical and skewed distributions. In a graphic representation of a frequency distribution the first obvious feature noticed is the symmetry or lack of symmetry in the figure. If the figure is perfectly symmetrical the mean, median and mode all coincide. If

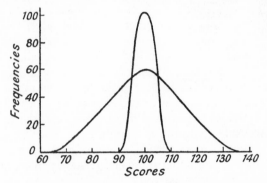

FIG. 5. TWO DISTRIBUTIONS WITH THE SAME MEAN BUT DIFFERENT RANGES AND DISPERSIONS

there is lack of symmetry, then the distribution is said to be skewed, and the mean, median and mode fall at different points.

Distributions that tail off towards the low values are said to be negatively skewed, and those with the opposite tendency positively skewed. These types of distribution are illustrated in Figs. 6 and 7 later in this chapter.

It is quite possible for two statistical distributions to have the same mean and the same total frequencies, and yet be skewed in opposite directions. Statisticians then have felt the need of devising a single coefficient to express the degree to which a distribution is skewed or the degree to which it lacks symmetry. Such a coefficient is the third numerical descriptive feature of frequency distributions.

It is the purpose of this chapter to explain and illustrate the methods of describing the dispersion and skewness of distributions by the use of single numbers.

The Total Range as a Measure of Dispersion. The

total *range* has been mentioned in an earlier chapter; it is the "distance" from the lowest to the highest. This total range is the simplest and most quickly ascertained indicator of variability. It is, however, the most unreliable, and should be used only for the purpose of preliminary inspection. In the illustration of the preceding section the range of output of the first group of factory workers was 110–90 or 20; the range of output of the second group was 135–65 or 70. This indicates that individual productivity in the second group is considerably more variable than in the first.

The range is unreliable because it is determined by only two measurements, all the other individual values in between having no effect on it. Quite often there is a gap between these extreme values and the next highest or lowest value. If these extreme cases had been missing from the sample there would have been a marked difference in the calculated range. When N, the number of cases per sample, is small, more often than not the extremes are marked by one case, and the range is a very unreliable indicator of variability. When N is large, possibly there is more than one case of each of the extreme measurements, and under these circumstances more attention may be paid to the range.

When data are grouped, the range is calculated by subtracting the lower limit of the bottom interval from the upper limit of the top interval.

The Quartile Deviation. The *quartile deviation* or *semi-interquartile range*, Q, is one-half of the range of the middle 50 per cent of the cases. Any individual case is as likely to fall within as outside the interquartile range. For this reason the quartile deviation is also known as the *probable error*. Quartile values divide the total range into four equal groups. The first quartile Q_1 is the point below which fall the first 25 per cent of the cases. The second quartile Q_2 is the point below which fall 50 per cent of the cases, and is, of course, the median. The third quartile Q_3 is the point below which lie 75 per cent of the cases, and above which fall the top 25 per cent.

The range from the first quartile to the third, that is $Q_3 - Q_1$, contains exactly half the cases, and this half is the middle half. This range is called the "interquartile range". It is divided by 2 to get the quartile deviation, a value often used to indicate variability.

The calculation of the quartiles and of the quartile deviation is illustrated in Table XI. The table shows the distribution of pass marks in an English examination scored by a sample of 120 students from a college.

TABLE XI. DISTRIBUTION OF PASS MARKS IN
ENGLISH EXAMINATION

Scores	f	
95–99	1	
90–94	2	
85–89	11	(14 cases to here)
80–84	18	← Q_3 interval
75–79	31	← Median, or Q_2 interval
70–74	21	(57 cases up to here)
65–69	13	← Q_1 interval
60–64	8	(23 cases to here)
55–59	8	
50–54	3	
45–49	2	
40–44	2	

$$N = 120$$

Lower Quartile, $Q_1 = 64 \cdot 5 + \dfrac{7}{13} \times 5 = 64 \cdot 5 + 2 \cdot 69 = 67 \cdot 19$

Upper Quartile, $Q_3 = 84 \cdot 5 - \dfrac{16}{18} \times 5 = 84 \cdot 5 - 4 \cdot 44 = 80 \cdot 06$

Quartile Deviation, $Q = (80 \cdot 06 - 67 \cdot 19)/2 = 12 \cdot 87/2 = 6 \cdot 43$

Median, $Q_2 = 74 \cdot 5 + \dfrac{3}{31} \times 5 = 74 \cdot 5 + 0 \cdot 48 = 74 \cdot 98$

The method is precisely the same as that used previously in calculating the median. For the first quartile Q_1, $N/4$ gives us 30. Counting up from the bottom we find that we need 7 cases from the 13 in the first quartile interval. The size of the interval is 5 so that $\frac{7}{13} \times 5$ gives 2·69. This is added on to the exact lower limit, 64·5, of this quartile interval, giving for Q_1 64·5 + 2·69, or 67·19. Counting down we note that 16 cases are needed from the third quartile interval. Thus $\frac{16}{18} \times 5$ gives 4·44, which has to be subtracted from 84·5, the exact upper limit of the third quartile interval. Q_3, then, is 84·5 − 4·44 or 80·06. The difference between Q_1 and Q_3 gives the inter-quartile range, and half of this gives the quartile deviation; this is (80·06 − 67·19) ÷ 2, which is 6·4.

The quartile deviation is a convenient measure of the scatter of a distribution. It indicates the degree of concentration of the measures, as it is the "range" that contains the middle half of the cases. When the quartile deviation is relatively large the measures are scattered, when it is small they are concentrated in the neighbourhood of the median. In reality, of course, it is not a deviation at all, being determined simply by counting along the scale in terms of cases. No average is calculated, and no particular deviation from any central point is involved. It is, however, a convenient device for pointing out the position of the middle half of the cases, and thus gives the same kind of information as those statistical measures which can be more accurately termed deviations.

The Mean Deviation. The quartile deviation just discussed only takes indirect account of the "form" of the distribution, of the relation between the values of particular measures and their frequency. There are two measures of variability that are directly concerned with the frequencies of each measure, the "mean deviation" and the "standard deviation".

Each of the measures in a distribution differs, or deviates, from the measure of central tendency. If a particular measure is greater than the average it has a positive deviation, if less, then it has a negative one. If all the deviations were calculated for all the measures, then the mean of their sum would give an excellent measure of the dispersion. If the measures were widely scattered their deviations would be relatively large, and so would be the mean of the deviations. If the measures were concentrated about the average then the mean of the deviations would be small.

This *mean deviation* (also known as the *mean variation*), then, is the third measure of the dispersion in a distribution. In calculating it the signs are ignored. The reason is obvious. In a perfectly symmetrical distribution the difference between positive and negative deviations from the median or mode would be zero, and in "any" distribution the algebraic sum of the deviations from the mean must always be zero. By disregarding the signs we ignore the direction which is of no importance to us here. We are only concerned with the amount of the deviation, and treat all differences as positive.

Calculation of the Mean Deviation from Ungrouped Data. The mean deviation or M.D., then, is the mean of the deviations of all the measures in a series taken from a measure

TABLE XII

CALCULATION OF M.D. FROM
UNGROUPED DATA

Col. 1 Score X	Col. 2 Deviation x
17	0·8
11	5·2
16	0·2
17	0·8
15	1·2
18	1·8
20	3·8
15	1·2
16	0·2
17	0·8
$\Sigma X = 162$	$\Sigma x = 16\cdot0$

$$M = 162/10 = 16\cdot2$$
$$M.D. = 16\cdot0/10 = 1\cdot6$$

of their central tendency, usually the arithmetic mean. It can be expressed in symbols for ungrouped data as

$$M.D. = \Sigma x/N$$

where Σx is the sum of the individual deviations. Table XII gives an illustration of its calculation.

The sum of the scores is 162, and as there are 10 cases, the arithmetic mean score is 162/10 or 16·2. Ignoring signs, this mean is then subtracted from each score to get the score's deviation; the deviations are listed in Column 2. The sum of the deviations is 16·0, and as their number is 10, the M.D. is 16·0/10 or 1·6.

Calculation of Mean Deviation from Grouped Data. When the data are grouped in a frequency distribution, again the mid-points of the classes are taken to represent the values in the classes. The formula for the mean deviation is now

$$M.D. = (\Sigma fx)/N$$

where, this time, x is the deviation of each mid-point from the mean of the distribution. The method is illustrated in Table XIII using the distribution of examination marks from Table XI.

The arithmetic mean of the distribution calculated by the short method (see Table VII) is 73·1. This is subtracted from the mid-point of each interval and the deviations x are listed in Column 4. Each deviation is multiplied by the frequency for that interval, and the fx products are entered in Column 5. The sum of the fx products, ignoring the signs, is 982·4. The M.D. is then this sum divided by N, which gives as a result 8·2.

What does this result mean? It means that on the average, the individual scores differed from the mean score of 73·1 by a little over 8. We may say further that, as the distribution is not too small and is also reasonably symmetrical, then, about 58 per cent of the cases fall within the limits of 1 M.D. below the mean and 1 M.D. above it, that is, in the range 65–81 approximately.

The Standard Deviation. By far the most important measure of dispersion is the standard deviation, denoted by σ (sigma). Its importance lies in the fact that statistically it is the most reliable. That is, it varies less than any other measure of variability from sample to sample, the samples being chosen at random from the same population. It is thus the most dependable value, and may be regarded as the most accurate estimate of the dispersion of the population.

TABLE XIII

CALCULATION OF MEAN DEVIATION FROM GROUPED DATA

Col. 1 Scores	Col. 2 Mid-points	Col. 3 f	Col. 4 x	Col. 5 fx
95–99	97	1	23·9	23·9
90–94	92	2	18·9	37·8
85–98	87	11	13·9	152·9
80–84	82	18	8·9	160·2
75–79	77	31	3·9	120·9
70–74	72	21	−1·1	23·1
65–69	67	13	−6·1	79·3
60–64	62	8	−11·1	88·8
55–59	57	8	−16·1	128·8
50–54	52	3	−21·1	63·3
45–49	47	2	−26·1	52·2
40–44	42	2	−31·1	62·2
		$N = 120$		$\Sigma fx = 982·4$

$$M = 73·1$$
$$\text{M.D.} = 982·4/120 = 8·2$$

The standard deviation is, like the mean deviation, a sort of average of all the deviations about the mean. It differs from the mean deviation in two important aspects. Firstly, in computing the standard deviation, the deviation of each measure from the mean is "squared". Secondly, the deviations are always taken from the arithmetic mean, whereas with the mean deviation they may be taken from the median also. Having squared the deviations these squares are then summed, and the sum is divided by N, the total number of cases in the distribution. From the result of this step the square root is extracted to give the standard deviation.

Calculation of σ from Ungrouped Data. The fundamental formula for the calculation of the standard deviation is

$$\sigma = \sqrt{(\Sigma x^2)/N}$$

where σ — standard deviation,
   x — deviation of a case from the mean,
   N — total frequency.

The calculation of σ from ungrouped data is illustrated in Table XIV: the data are those of Table XII in an earlier part of the chapter. As before, the deviations from the mean of 16·2 are calculated and listed in Column 2. These x values are

TABLE XIV

CALCULATION OF σ FROM UNGROUPED DATA

Col. 1 X	Col. 2 x	Col. 3 x^2
17	0·8	0·64
11	−5·2	27·04
16	−0·2	0·04
17	0·8	0·64
15	−1·2	1·44
18	1·8	3·24
20	3·8	14·44
15	−1·2	1·44
16	−0·2	0·04
17	0·8	0·64
162		49·60

$M = 16·2$

$\sigma = \sqrt{49·60/10} = \sqrt{4·960} = 2·22$

squared and the squares are entered in Column 3. The sum of the squares, that is, Σx^2 is 49·60. This is divided by 10, the total number of cases, and the square root of the result gives a standard deviation of 2·22.

When the deviations are squared, the extreme values, because they are the largest, gain an added weight. This emphasis of the extreme items means that the standard deviation will always be somewhat larger than the mean deviation calculated from the same series. In one important aspect, however, the mean and standard deviations are similar. Both take into account the absolute value of each individual item in the distribution.

We have already said that it may be taken that approximately 58 per cent of the total number of cases fall in the range of 1 M.D. below and 1 M.D. above the mean. It will be seen later that in many distributions approximately two-thirds of the cases fall within the range of one standard deviation on either side of the mean. These statements apply, of course, more accurately to samples containing large numbers. For example suppose the average I.Q. of children at a school had been calculated as 101·2 with a σ of 9·3. This means that approximately two-thirds of the pupils fall within the range 101·2 ± 9·3; that is within the range 91·9 to 110·5. This example illustrates the importance in the interpretation of statistical data, not only of an average value, but also of a measure of dispersion.

Calculation of σ from Grouped Data. By far the greater part of statistical calculation is concerned with data grouped into class intervals. Because the standard deviation is an important statistic, its computation from grouped data will be described carefully step by step. The procedure is illustrated in Table XV which deals again with the distribution of examination marks from the example earlier in this chapter. The formula for the calculation is

$$\sigma = i \sqrt{\frac{\Sigma f x'^2}{N} - c'^2}$$

where i — size of class interval,

x' — deviation from the guessed mean in terms of class intervals,

c' — the correction factor in terms of class intervals.

TABLE XV

CALCULATION OF STANDARD DEVIATION FROM GROUPED DATA

Col. 1 Scores	Col. 2 Mid-point	Col. 3 f	Col. 4 x'	Col. 5 fx'	Col. 6 fx'^2
95–99	97	1	4	4	16
90–94	92	2	3	6	18
85–89	87	11	2	22	44
80–84	82	18	1	18	18
75–79	A.M. 77	31	0	—— + 50	
70–74	72	21	−1	−21	21
65–69	67	13	−2	−26	52
60–64	62	8	−3	−24	72
55–59	57	8	−4	−32	128
50–54	52	3	−5	−15	75
45–49	47	2	−6	−12	72
40–44	42	2	−7	−14 —— − 144	98
		$N = 120$		$\Sigma fx' = -94$	$\Sigma fx'^2 = 614$

A.M. $= 77$

$$c' = \frac{\Sigma fx'}{N} = \frac{-94}{120}$$

$$c = ic' = \frac{-94}{120} \times 5$$

$$= -3.92$$

$$M = \text{A.M.} + c$$

$$= 77 - 3.92$$

$$= 73.1$$

$$\sigma = 5 \times \sqrt{\frac{614}{120} - \left(-\frac{94}{120}\right)^2}$$

$$= 5 \times \sqrt{5.116 - 0.613}$$

$$= 5 \times 2.112$$

$$= 10.56$$

1. The first part of the computation is the short method for calculating the mean illustrated in the previous chapter. In

this example there is no need actually to calculate the true mean, but the correction factor is required. This is calculated as before, giving a value for c' of $-94/120$. It is noted that c' is the correction factor in terms of class intervals.

2. For each interval the product fx'^2 is required. This is obtained by multiplying the fx' value in Column 5 by the x' value in Column 4. The products are listed in Column 6.

3. The fx'^2 products in Column 6 are summed giving $\Sigma fx'^2$. In the table this is 614.

4. This sum is to be divided by N the total frequency to give $(\Sigma fx'^2)/N$, or $614/120$.

5. From this must be subtracted the square of the correction factor c', or $\left(\dfrac{-94}{120}\right)^2$. The calculation has now become $614/120 - (94/120)^2$.

6. The square root must now be extracted from the result of the previous step. This gives $2 \cdot 112$.

7. As all the computation has up to now been carried out in terms of class intervals, the $2 \cdot 112$ must be multiplied by the size of the class interval to give the standard deviation in terms of measures or scores. The final result is then $5 \times 2 \cdot 112$ or $10 \cdot 56$.

The table illustrates the complete calculation of the arithmetic mean and the standard deviation, probably the most important and commonest statistical computation from data grouped into a frequency distribution. As the arithmetic mean is the most widely used measure of central tendency, so the standard deviation is the most widely used measure of dispersion. It is well adapted to further statistical computations such as encountered in correlation work, as will be shown in a later chapter.

When to Use the Various Measures of Variability. When deciding which measure of variability to use in a particular situation several factors need to be considered. If statistical reliability is the important desired feature, then the order of choice is the standard deviation, the mean deviation, the quartile deviation, and the total range. If on the other hand ease and rapidity of computation is desired then the order is reversed. An important consideration is whether further statistical computation is going to be made. If so, then the standard deviation is the one to use, as will be seen in later work.

If a distribution has an unusual number of extreme measures at one or both ends of the range, then maybe the mean deviation will be preferred to the standard deviation. This is because the squaring of the deviations might give undue weight to the extremes. The same choice might be preferred in the case of a heavily skewed distribution for the same reason.

The quartile deviation takes no note of the extremes, and gives great importance to the middle of the range. In general it is used when the median is chosen as the measure of central tendency.

The following summary will serve as a guide to the selection of a measure of dispersion in a particular situation.

1. Use the range:
    (a) for the quickest indication of dispersion,
    (b) when information of the total spread is all that is required.
2. Use the quartile deviation:
    (a) when using the median for central tendency,
    (b) when there are few very extreme measures,
    (c) for a relatively quick inspectional measure of dispersion.
3. Use the mean deviation:
    (a) for a fairly reliable measure, avoiding the work involved in computing the standard deviation,
    (b) when extremes should be considered but not stressed.
4. Use the standard deviation:
    (a) for the measure with the highest reliability,
    (b) when further computations depending on it are needed,
    (c) when it is desired that extreme deviations should have a proportionally greater influence on the measure of dispersion.

Skewness. In this and the preceding chapter we have discussed measures of central tendency and of dispersion. One gives an estimate of the "typical" value of a series, and the other gives an indication of the extent to which the items cluster around or scatter away from that typical value.

We must now concern ourselves with a statistical measure that will indicate whether the distribution is symmetrical, or tails off in one direction or the other. The measure is called the *coefficient of skewness*.

Relationships among Measures of Central Tendency and Skewness. We have already seen that when data are distributed symmetrically, the mean, median and mode have identical values. When skewness appears, however, these averages pull apart with the arithmetic mean, the median and the mode falling at different points.

It is important to know whether any skewness indicated in a distribution is a real divergence from the symmetrical form, or whether it is merely due to chance factors arising from the particular sample chosen. A measure of the degree of skewness can be calculated by considering the mean and the median.

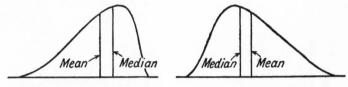

FIG. 6. NEGATIVE SKEWNESS FIG. 7. POSITIVE SKEWNESS

The more nearly the distribution is symmetrical, the closer will be the mean and the median, and the less the skewness. When the values tend to pile up at the high end of the scale as in Fig. 6, and spread out gradually towards the low end of the scale, then the distribution is negatively skewed. In this case, as the figure shows, the median has a greater value than the mean. The opposite tendency illustrated in Fig. 7 is when the values tend to pile up towards the low end of the scale, tailing off towards the high end. This is called positive skewness, and here the mean has a greater value than the median.

Calculation of Coefficient of Skewness. By considering the relation between the values of these two averages, the mean and the median, we can achieve a measure that will indicate the degree of skewness of a distribution and also its direction. The formula is

$$Sk = \frac{3(Mean - Median)}{\sigma}$$

If the mean is larger than the median, the sign will be plus, indicating that the series is positively skewed and the values tail off towards the high end of the scale. When the median is larger than the mean, the coefficient will have a negative sign, indicating that the individual values tend to tail off towards the low end of the scale, i.e. that there is negative skewness.

The absolute difference between the mean and the median will, of course, depend on the units used as well as upon the

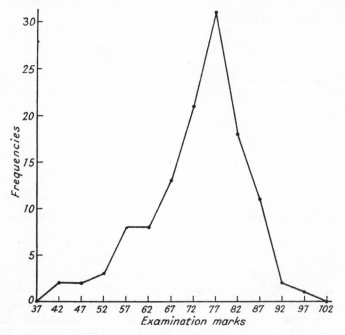

FIG. 8. DISTRIBUTION OF EXAMINATION MARKS IN THE FORM OF A FREQUENCY POLYGON

skewness of the series. In order to achieve a number that will be independent of the size of the unit and that will enable a comparison of skewness of two different distributions, the absolute difference is suitably expressed as a fraction of the standard deviation of the series.

As an example of calculating the coefficient, consider the distribution of examination marks used earlier in the chapter. Table XI shows that the calculation of the median results in a value of 74·98. Table XV gives 73·1 for the mean and 10·56 for the standard deviation. Thus

$$Sk = 3(73·1 - 74·98)/10·56$$
$$= 3(-1·88)/10·56$$
$$= -5·64/10·56 = -0·53$$

This result indicates a relatively large amount of negative skewness; that is, the series tails off towards the left, to the low values. The distribution is plotted as a frequency polygon in Fig. 8 and the lack of symmetry is readily noted.

The really important question, however, remains to be answered. Is the degree of skewness shown in our sample "significant"? Can we predict that the total population distribution will be skewed to the same degree and in the same direction as in our sample? This question can be readily answered. The answer however depends on the calculation of a "standard error". In fact all the statistics of a distribution require the computation of "standard errors" before predictions about population may be made from samples. This important topic will be dealt with in a later chapter.

We now have statistical tools which describe the central tendency, the dispersion, and the skewness of a distribution. With these we may obtain a reasonably adequate statistical description of any homogeneous body of data.

CHAPTER IV

Cumulative Distributions

In the simple frequency distribution discussed in Chapter I, the frequency of each class interval is shown separately. The total number of cases in the group is found by adding up the frequencies recorded in each class interval. Such a method of organising a mass of data into class intervals, we have found very useful. From such tables we can learn, for example, the number of factory workers between forty and forty-five years of age, the number of students who scored between 50 and 60 marks in a test, the number of employees earning between £8 and £9 a week, the number of workers who can produce between 30 and 40 units per day, and so on.

In the present chapter we shall be concerned with a different way of presenting the facts. The difference is not in the organisation of the data, but in the manner of presenting it. The data are still organised into class intervals as before, but the form of the frequency distribution is changed from a simple distribution into a cumulative one.

There is no added merit attached in this. It is just an alternative method to be used when information is required in a certain form. For example, a sociologist might be interested in knowing how many people "more than" or "less than" forty years of age work in the factories in a particular area. An education officer might wish to know how many children score "more than" or "less than" a certain mark in a test. A wages arbitration board may require to know how many individuals in a certain occupation earn "less than" a certain amount; while an economist may be interested in the number of factories that produce "over a certain production figure" per year.

The cumulative form of the frequency distribution is well adapted to answering questions posed in this "more than" or "less than" manner. As the term suggests, we cumulate the frequencies to see how many items are "more than" or "less than" a certain amount.

TABLE XVI

AGE DISTRIBUTION OF MALE FACTORY WORKERS

CORPORATION X

(Col. 1) Age Group	(Col. 2) Frequency No. of Men	Cumulative Frequencies	
		(Col. 3) More than	(Col. 4) Less than
75–79	40	40	20,000
70–74	206	246	19,960
65–69	516	762	19,754
60–64	822	1,584	19,238
55–59	1,277	2,861	18,416
50–54	1,856	4,717	17,139
45–49	2,310	7,027	15,283
40–44	2,414	9,441	12,973
35–39	2,475	11,916	10,559
30–34	2,455	14,371	8,084
25–29	2,744	17,115	5,629
20–24	2,414	19,529	2,885
15–19	471	20,000	471

$$\Sigma = 20,000 = N$$

Types of Cumulative Frequency Distribution. Table XVI shows the age distribution of 20,000 workers employed in the factories of a large industrial corporation. The data are hypothetical.

Now from these data we wish to answer three questions.

Firstly, the corporation is considering the establishment of a pension scheme for its factory workers. An individual will qualify for a pension at the age of sixty-five, and it is required to know how many of the workers are sixty-five or over. Secondly the personnel department feels that it is doubtful whether there is room for employment for older men in the factories, and would like to know how many workers are in fact over forty years of age. Finally, if in case of a national emergency, workers in the industry up to the age of, say, thirty will be conscripted, how many of the corporation's factory employees will be affected?

In order to answer the first two questions, it is necessary to construct a cumulative frequency distribution of the "more than" type, while to answer the third, a cumulative distribution of the "less than" type is needed.

Constructing a "more than" Cumulative Frequency Distribution. In Table XVI we find that there are forty workers whose ages are more than seventy-five years. Forty, then, appears at the top of Column 3. We next find that there are 206 workers whose ages range between seventy and seventy-four. The total number of employees aged seventy years or over is then 40 + 206, or 246. This is the second item in Column 3. 516 workers have ages ranging from sixty-five to sixty-nine. Adding this to the accumulated frequencies for the two higher classes, we find that 40 + 206 + 516, or 762 workers are sixty-five years of age or more. And so it goes on, each cumulative frequency being the sum of the previous one and of the frequency in the class interval itself. This continues until the last, in this case the lowest, interval is reached. The last cumulative frequency should be equal to N; if it is not, a mistake has been made. In our example there are 20,000 workers who are fifteen years of age or more.

When the frequencies have been accumulated in this way, the distribution shown in Column 3 of the table is secured. We can now readily answer our first two questions. There are 762 workers aged over sixty-five who would qualify for a pension. There are 9,441, or approximately 50 per cent, who are forty or more.

Plotting a "more than" Cumulative Distribution. Fig. 9 shows the cumulative frequencies plotted against the corresponding age groups. The method of plotting is similar to that used in plotting the simple frequency distribution, except that here we never use the histogram type of graph.

The age groups or class intervals are marked off along the base line, and on the vertical axis the cumulated frequencies are laid off. As before, the height of the curve should be approximately 75 per cent of its width. When plotting the frequency polygon, the frequency in each interval is taken at the "mid-point" of the interval. In the "more than"

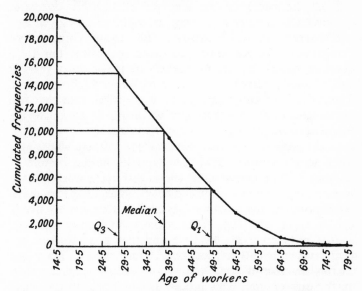

FIG. 9. CUMULATIVE "MORE THAN" AGE DISTRIBUTION OF MALE
FACTORY WORKERS

cumulative frequency curve, however, each cumulative frequency is plotted at the "exact lower limit" of the interval. The reason becomes clear when we consider the lowest age group or interval. There are 20,000 workers, all of whom are fifteen years of age or older. They are not all older than seventeen, the mid-point of the interval, and we know that only 19,529 are older than nineteen, the upper limit of the interval. Thus in order to state the age exceeded by the 20,000 workers, the mid-point value is no use; neither is the upper limit. Clearly, the lower class limit is required.

In plotting the data, therefore, the frequency of 20,000 is

plotted directly over 14·5, the exact lower limit of the first interval; 19,529 over 19·5, the exact lower limit of the interval 20–24; 17,115 over 24·5, and so on. When all the cumulated frequencies have been plotted the points are joined by straight lines. To bring the curve down to the base line, the cumulative frequency of o is plotted at the "upper exact limit" of the interval 75–79. This means that there are no workers of age "more than" 79·5 years.

From this curve we can now read off to a fair degree of accuracy the number of workers who exceed any given age.

Constructing and Plotting a "less than" Cumulative Frequency Distribution. In order to answer our third question, namely how many workers are of age thirty years or less, we need a "less than" cumulative frequency distribution. The method of constructing this is identical with that just demonstrated, except that now we begin to cumulate the frequencies from the other end of the scale.

In the table we find that there are 471 workers whose ages are nineteen or less. 471, then, appears at the bottom of Column 4. The next interval shows that 2,414 workers have ages ranging between twenty and twenty-four. The total number of workers, then, whose ages are less than twenty-five is 471 + 2,414, or 2,885. This is the second entry from the bottom in Column 4. Next we find that 2,744 workers are aged between twenty-five and twenty-nine years. This makes the total number of 2,744 + 2,885, or 5,629 who are less than thirty years of age. This process is continued up the scale, each cumulative frequency being the sum of the cumulative frequency up to the interval immediately below it and the frequency for the particular interval. At the top of the column we find, as we expect, that there are 20,000 workers whose ages are less than eighty years.

From this cumulative distribution we get a ready answer to our query. 5,629 of the workers would be subject to conscription in time of emergency. It will be noted that this figure is the cumulative frequency for the interval 25–29. The reason is that "less than" cumulative frequencies refer to the "upper limit" of the class interval. Again this is readily understood by referring to the lowest interval 15–19. We do not know how many individuals are of age less than seventeen years, the mid-point of the interval. No worker is less than fifteen years of age, the lower limit. We only know that 471 are less than twenty years of age.

Fig. 10 shows the "less than" cumulative frequencies plotted in the form of a graph. As just indicated, they are plotted above the "exact upper limits" of the intervals. Thus, there are 20,000 workers whose ages are less than 79·5 years, 19,960 below 74·5 years, 19,754 below 69·5 years, and so on. The graph is again brought down to the base line by placing the cumulative frequency of 0 at the "lower exact limit" of the bottom interval, that is 14·5. There are no workers less than 14·5 years of age.

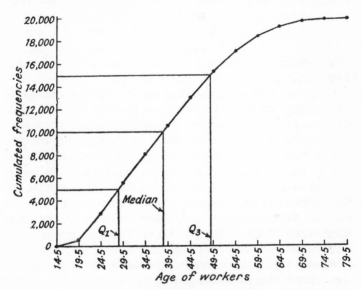

FIG. 10. CUMULATIVE "LESS THAN" AGE DISTRIBUTION OF MALE FACTORY WORKERS

If for any purpose the number of workers less than a certain age is required the information is readily available from the graph.

It is interesting to note that from this type of graph the median and the quartiles are readily available. To find the median, we first locate the frequency of $N/2$, i.e., 10,000 on the vertical axis. From this point a horizontal line is drawn to intersect the curve. From the point of intersection a perpen-

dicular is dropped to the base. Where this cuts the base line
the median value can be read off. On ordinary graph paper
this value can be determined accurately to one place of
decimals. For example, the median value on the "less than"
curve in Fig. 10, is 38·5. This means that of the total group of
workers, 10,000 are older than 38·5 years, and 10,000 younger.
It is the middle age. As would be expected, this identical
median value is extracted also from the "more than" curve.
In fact "more than" and "less than" curves when plotted
on the same base always intersect at the median value, or 50
per cent mark, as it is sometimes called. Q_1 and Q_2 are
similarly determined by drawing horizontal lines from
frequencies of 5,000 and 15,000 respectively. The quartiles,
of course, are not the same for the two curves.

Distribution of Cumulative Percentages. In an
earlier chapter we pointed out the value of transforming
frequencies into percentages for the sake of comparing two
distributions where the N-values differ. The transformation
has a similar usefulness when we are dealing with cumulative
frequencies. Two cumulative distributions plotted on the
same base line would reveal little if they differed markedly in
size due to different total frequencies. For example, we
might wish to compare the age distribution of the male
factory workers in Corporation X, with that for the female
factory workers of whom there were seven thousand. To
present this comparison graphically in a form that will
emphasise the basic differences between the distributions, the
frequencies are transformed into percentages.

The method of transformation is shown in Table XVII.
The table contains the data giving the age distribution of our
factory workers. The frequencies are cumulated on the "less
than" principle, as in Table XVI, and are listed in Column 4.
We now wish to change these into percentages. All that is
necessary is to multiply each cumulative frequency by $100/N$,
or in this case 100/20,000, or 1/200. This has been done and
the results are listed in Column 5 interval by interval.

Thus 100 per cent or all the workers are less than 79·5 years
old, the upper limit of the top interval. 85·69 per cent are less
than 54·5 years of age, 40·42 per cent less than 34·5 years, and
so on. In actual practice the cumulative percentages need not
be given to more than one place of decimals. In Fig. 11 the

TABLE XVII

CUMULATIVE PERCENTAGE AGE DISTRIBUTION OF MALE FACTORY WORKERS

Col. 1	Col. 2	Col. 3	Col. 4	Col. 5
Age Group	Exact Upper Limit	f	cf	Cumulative Percentage
75–79	79·5	40	20,000	100
70–74	74·5	206	19,960	99·80
65–69	69·5	516	19,754	98·77
60–64	64·5	822	19,238	96·19
55–59	59·5	1,277	18,416	92·08
50–54	54·5	1,856	17,139	85·69
45–49	49·5	2,310	15,283	76·41
40–44	44·5	2,414	12,973	64·86
35–39	39·5	2,475	10,559	52·79
30–34	34·5	2,455	8,084	40·42
25–29	29·5	2,744	5,629	28·14
20–24	24·5	2,414	2,885	14·42
15–19	19·5	471	471	2·35

cumulative percentages just obtained are plotted as points against the corresponding exact upper limits of the age group intervals. Again we get an S-shaped curve. Our curve now, however, is standardised as to height. Any other age distribution, irrespective of its total frequency, plotted on the same base must have the same height. The 100 per cent mark is the ceiling for all. Such a standardised curve is known as an *ogive*. The ogive is, in other words, the cumulative percentage distribution curve. Two ogives are by virtue of their common height much more readily comparable than two ordinary cumulative distribution curves.

Use of the Ogive for Comparison. As an illustration of the use of the ogive for purposes of comparison, consider the data set out in Table XVIII. The table shows the scores obtained by two groups of twelve-year-old children in a mechanical arithmetic test. One group consisted of 300 girls, the other of 300 boys. The ogives for these data are given in Fig. 12.

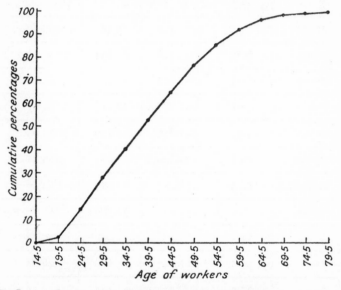

FIG. 11. CUMULATIVE PERCENTAGE AGE DISTRIBUTION OF MALE FACTORY WORKERS

Much useful information is readily available from the graphical presentation of these cumulative frequency distributions. The ogive for the boys lies to the right of that for the girls over the entire range of scores. Thus the boys score consistently higher than the girls. The extent of the difference in achievement between the two groups is shown by the distance apart of the two curves. This varies at different levels. At the extremes the differences between the very high-scoring and very low-scoring boys and girls are not very large. Over the middle range of scores the differences are more marked.

TABLE XVIII

CUMULATIVE DISTRIBUTIONS FROM MECHANICAL ARITHMETIC TEST SCORES OF BOYS AND GIRLS

Scores	Exact Upper Limit	f Boys	Cumulative f	Cumulative %	f Girls	Cumulative f	Cumulative %
60–64	64·5	1	300	100·0	0	300	100·0
55–59	59·5	2	299	99·7	1	300	100·0
50–54	54·5	30	297	99·0	12	299	99·7
45–49	49·5	72	267	89·0	39	287	95·7
40–44	44·5	69	195	65·0	60	248	82·7
35–39	39·5	38	126	42·0	63	188	62·7
30–34	34·5	39	88	29·3	55	125	41·7
25–29	29·5	22	49	16·3	23	70	23·3
20–24	24·5	14	27	9·0	28	47	15·7
15–19	19·5	10	13	4·3	8	19	6·3
10–14	14·5	3	3	1·0	5	11	3·7
5–9	9·5	0	0	0·0	6	6	2·0
0–4	4·5	0	0	0·0	0	0	0·0

A more exact comparison of the two groups can be obtained by considering the medians and quartiles. The boys' median is approximately 41, while that of the girls is approximately 36. The difference between the two median values is given in the figure by the length of the line *AB*. Similarly the differences at the first and third quartiles are given by the lengths of lines *EF* and *CD* respectively. It is clear that the groups differ a little more markedly at the median and upper quartile level, than at the level of the lower quartile.

By extending the vertical line through *B*, the median value for the boys' group, we see that approximately 70 per cent of the girls' group score less than this mark. Thus, only 30 per cent of the girls achieve a mark above the median value of the boys in mechanical arithmetic. Conversely, 34 per cent of the boys score less than the median value for the girls; that is 76 per cent of the boys exceed the girls' median. In a similar manner the difference between the two groups at any level, or the overlap at any point on the range of scores, is readily available.

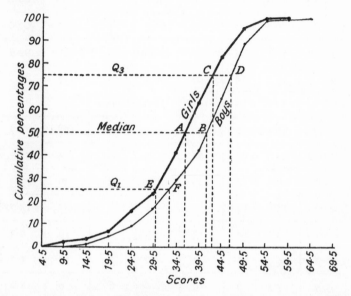

FIG. 12. CUMULATIVE PERCENTAGE SCORE DISTRIBUTIONS FOR BOYS AND GIRLS IN MECHANICAL ARITHMETIC TEST

This illustration clearly indicates the value for comparative purposes of transforming cumulative frequencies into cumulative percentages.

Calculation of Centiles in a Distribution. We have already learned that the median is the point in a frequency distribution below which lie 50 per cent of the cases; and that the quartiles Q_1 and Q_3 are the points below which lie 25 per cent and 75 per cent of the cases respectively. Using exactly the same method as that used in calculating the median and quartiles, we can calculate *centile points*. A centile point is a value on the scoring or measuring scale below which falls any given percentage of cases. Thus the 84th centile is the point below which fall 84 per cent of the cases, and the 40th centile is the point below which fall 40 per cent of the cases. Using this terminology the median becomes the 50th centile, and the upper and lower quartiles the 75th and 25th centiles respectively.

Centiles are extensively used in education, educational psychology, and other fields where tests of varying kinds are given to relatively large numbers of individuals. Their value may be demonstrated by an example. A student in a university entrance examination scored, say, 65 in Mathematics, 140 in English, and 73 in Physics. What information may be gained from these raw scores? In fact very little. It is impossible without further knowledge to assess the student's achievements in the three subjects. If, however, further information were available to the effect that 85 in Mathematics is at the 94th centile, 140 in English at the 53rd centile, and 73 in Physics at the 31st centile, and these centiles were established by the marks of 1,200 applicants, then a very informative picture is presented. Relative to his fellows our student is very highly placed in Mathematics, moderately lowly placed in Physics, and is about average in English. The use of centiles, then, enables us to do two things. First it enables us to assess the general level of a score in a known population, and secondly it transforms the scores for different tests into a form in which they are readily comparable.

As an example of the method of calculating the centiles let us use the scores achieved by the twelve-year-old boys in the mechanical arithmetic test. The computation is shown in full in Table XIX.

The particular centile points calculated are the 90th, 80th, 70th, etc., or as they are called, the *deciles*. As the method of computation is identical with that for computing the median and quartiles, the reader is advised to look back and check up on that method.

The table shows in Column 1 the deciles or centile points to be calculated. The first thing we must do is to find the number of cases we shall have to include in any given percentage. There were altogether 300 boys. Ten per cent of 300 is 30. Thirty boys then fall below the 10th centile. The number falling below each centile point is shown in

TABLE XIX
CALCULATION OF CENTILES
FROM MECHANICAL ARITHMETIC TEST DATA

Col. 1	Col. 2	Col. 3	Col. 4		Col. 5
% below Centile Point	No. below Centile Point	Cumu-lative Frequency below Centile Interval	Lower Exact Limit of Centile Interval	Height of Centile Point above this Lower Limit	Centile Point Pn
90	270	267	$49 \cdot 5 \; +$	$\dfrac{3 \times 5}{30}$	50·0
80	240	195	$44 \cdot 5 \; +$	$\dfrac{45 \times 5}{72}$	47·62
70	210	195	$44 \; 5 \; +$	$\dfrac{15 \times 5}{72}$	45·54
60	180	126	$39 \cdot 5 \; +$	$\dfrac{54 \times 5}{69}$	43·41
50	150	126	$39 \cdot 5 \; +$	$\dfrac{24 \times 5}{69}$	41·27
40	120	88	$34 \cdot 5 \; +$	$\dfrac{32 \times 5}{38}$	38·72
30	90	88	$34 \cdot 5 \; +$	$\dfrac{2 \times 5}{38}$	34·76
20	60	49	$29 \cdot 5 \; +$	$\dfrac{11 \times 5}{39}$	30·91
10	30	27	$24 \cdot 5 \; +$	$\dfrac{3 \times 5}{22}$	25·18

Column 2. We see, for example, that 270 boys fall below the 90th centile.

To continue the calculation for the 90th centile, we must now find the point on the scale below which lie 270 cases. Referring to Table XVIII we find that the 270th case falls somewhere in the score interval 50–54. The cumulated frequencies up to this interval total 267. Column 3 of Table XVIII indicates the cumulative frequency actually below the interval containing the centile point.

The exact lower limit of the interval 50–54 which contains the 90th centile is 49·5. We need 3 more cases out of the 30 in this interval to make up the 270. There are 5 score units in the interval, so we have to advance $\frac{3}{30}$ times 5, or as shown in Column 4 of Table XIX, we add $3 \times 5/30$ to 49·5, the exact lower limit of the interval. This gives a score value of 50 as the 90th centile point, or, using the usual notation, P_{90} equals 50.

The other centile points in the table are calculated in exactly the same manner; they are listed in Column 5 of the table. If a score value which is not listed were required, then its equivalent centile position would be estimated by interpolation. For example, a score of 42 would be at approximately the 55th centile, and a score of 46 at the 75th centile. The reader is advised to check through the calculation of the other centile points so that he may become thoroughly acquainted with the method.

CHAPTER V

The Normal Distribution Curve

Frequency Distributions in Practice and in Theory.
Thus far we have dealt with frequency distributions based
upon data obtained from observation and experiment.
Distribution curves so obtained often approximate curves
which are derived from purely theoretical considerations, and
not infrequently the degree of approximation is a close one.
A theoretical distribution curve which is of fundamental
importance is the so-called normal curve.

We shall not give a rigorous derivation of the normal curve.
Nevertheless, it will be shown how the normal distribution
curve may be arrived at. We shall then indicate in what way
this theoretical distribution is of practical importance in the
social sciences. Finally, we shall study in some detail the
properties of the normal distribution.

Probability and Binomial Distributions. Customarily,
coin-tossing has been used as a vehicle for the introduction to
the elements of probability. It might seem to the reader that
coin-tossing has little to do with practical problems. True as
this may be, a consideration of how tossed coins will fall can
conveniently illustrate some fundamental theory. Using it at
the outset, we shall be able to avoid confronting the reader with
the unfamiliar and, perhaps, estranging language of mathematics.

We must assume to be dealing with coins which are ideally
uniform and symmetrical. That is, each of our coins has no
tendency whatever to fall more often on one side than on the
other; in other words, there are absolutely even chances of
heads or tails. We may then say that there is one chance in two
(1:2) or a probability of 0·5 of throwing heads; the probability
of tails is, of course, the same.

Consider now two such coins, say A and B, being tossed

simultaneously. There are four equally likely probabilities. There is 1 chance in 4 of *A*-heads and *B*-tails, 1 chance in 4 of *A*-tails and *B*-heads, and 1 in 4, each, of both being heads or both being tails. Thus, there is 1 chance in 4 of both heads, 1 chance in 4 of both tails and 2 chances in 4 (or 1 chance in 2) of one being heads and the other tails. These probabilities may be set out as shown in Table XX.

TABLE XX

DISTRIBUTION OF CHANCES OF FALLS OF 2 COINS TOSSED 4 TIMES

Two Coins	Two Heads (2H)	One Heads (1H) and One Tails (1T)	Two Tails (2T)
Number of chances in four	1	2	1

Next, toss three coins simultaneously. By a reasoning similar to the above it is easy to see that the four probabilities will now be as set out in Table XXI.

TABLE XXI

DISTRIBUTION OF CHANCES OF FALLS OF 3 COINS TOSSED 8 TIMES

Three Coins	3H	2H 1T	1H 2T	3T
Number of chances in eight	1	3	3	1

Tossing four, five, six, seven, eight, nine and ten coins at a time, the probabilities of the distribution of falls in each case are as shown in Table XXII.

TABLE XXII. PROBABILITIES OF FALLS OF 4 TO 10 COINS

4 COINS	4H	3H 1T	2H 2T	1H 3T	4T						
No. of chances in 16	1	4	6	4	1						

5 COINS	5H	4H 1T	3H 2T	2H 3T	1H 4T	5T					
No. of chances in 32	1	5	10	10	5	1					

6 COINS	6H	5H 1T	4H 2T	3H 3T	2H 4T	1H 5T	6T				
No. of chances in 64	1	6	15	20	15	6	1				

7 COINS	7H	6H 1T	5H 2T	4H 3T	3H 4T	2H 5T	1H 6T	7T			
No. of chances in 128	1	7	21	35	35	21	7	1			

8 COINS	8H	7H 1T	6H 2T	5H 3T	4H 4T	3H 5T	2H 6T	1H 7T	8T		
No. of chances in 256	1	8	28	56	70	56	28	8	1		

9 COINS	9H	8H 1T	7H 2T	6H 3T	5H 4T	4H 5T	3H 6T	2H 7T	1H 8T	9T	
No. of chances in 512	1	9	36	84	126	126	84	36	9	1	

10 COINS	10H	9H 1T	8H 2T	7H 3T	6H 4T	5H 5T	4H 6T	3H 7T	2H 8T	1H 9T	10T
No. of chances in 1,024	1	10	45	120	210	252	210	120	45	10	1

Now plot one of the chance distributions of throws in the form of a histogram. The dotted columns in Fig. 13 show the distribution of throws when ten coins are tossed simultaneously. We can also join the mid-points of the columns, as shown by the unbroken line superposed upon the histogram. The height of each column thus represents the number of chances in 1,024, corresponding to the conditions set out along the base.

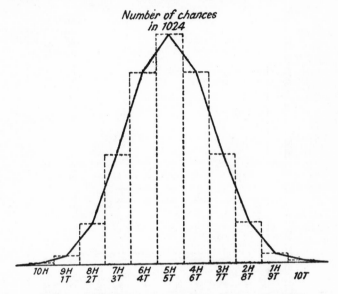

FIG. 13. THE BINOMIAL DISTRIBUTION OF $(1+1)^{10}$

Consider for a moment the frequency distributions as set out in Tables XX, XXI and XXII in conjunction with the following simple algebraic identities, the so-called binomial expansions:

$$(a + b)^2 = a^2 + 2ab + b^2$$
$$(a + b)^3 = a^3 + 3a^2b + 3ab^2 + b^3$$
$$(a + b)^4 = a^4 + 4a^3b + 6a^2b^2 + 4ab^3 + b^4$$
$$(a + b)^5 = a^5 + 5a^4b + 10a^3b^2 + 10a^2b^3 + 5ab^4 + b^5, \text{ etc.}$$

Note that the coefficients of the binomial expansions correspond to the frequency distributions set out earlier. In fact, putting $a = 1$ and $b = 1$, we can set out the expansions as shown in Table XXIII, so that the numbers to the right of the equals signs correspond to the chance distributions of Table XXII. It is thus clear why such probability distributions are known as *binomial distributions*.

Table XXIII

Expansions of $(1 + 1)^n$ (where n is a positive integer)

$$(1+1)^2 = 1 + 2 + 1$$
$$(1+1)^3 = 1 + 3 + 3 + 1$$
$$(1+1)^4 = 1 + 4 + 6 + 4 + 1$$
$$(1+1)^5 = 1 + 5 + 10 + 10 + 5 + 1$$
$$(1+1)^6 = 1 + 6 + 15 + 20 + 15 + 6 + 1$$
$$(1+1)^7 = 1 + 7 + 21 + 35 + 35 + 21 + 7 + 1$$
$$(1+1)^8 = 1 + 8 + 28 + 56 + 70 + 56 + 28 + 8 + 1$$
$$(1+1)^9 = 1 + 9 + 36 + 84 + 126 + 126 + 84 + 36 + 9 + 1$$
$$(1+1)^{10} = 1 + 10 + 45 + 120 + 210 + 252 + 210 + 120 + 45 + 10 + 1$$

Normal Distributions. We have seen that for ten coins to be tossed all at once, the probabilities of the eleven different falls can easily be worked out. In circumstances which must be regarded as ideal, if we were, in fact, to toss 10 coins in this manner 1,024 times, we could expect the 11 types of falls to be so distributed that their numbers correspond to the binomial expansions of $(1+1)^{10}$.

Imagine now that we are to toss a large number, say, n coins all at once. The number of arrangements of heads and tails in which the coins can fall will, of course, also be correspondingly large. Plot then the probable frequency distributions of these arrangements. If there are n coins, there will be $(n + 1)$ arrangements, and they will be distributed according to the $(1 + 1)^n$ binomial expansion.

Now imagine n becoming larger and larger. If we were to plot the corresponding binomial frequency distributions, we should have more and more points defining our curves. If we were to use a sheet of square paper and attempt to superpose our curves upon one another using the same base, as n increases we should approach closer and closer to what is termed a *normal curve*, such as is shown in Fig. 14.

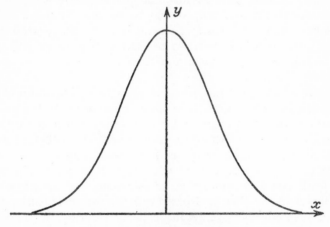

FIG. 14. NORMAL CURVE

It ought to be noted that, strictly, there is not just one normal curve, but a whole set of curves of the same general form. We shall deal with this at a later stage.

A binomial distribution is a distribution of discrete quantities — heads and tails arrangements in the case of our example. Thus, there is not a truly continuous, smooth curve corresponding to such a distribution. On the other hand, a normal curve is a smooth one. It can be regarded as representing a continuous relationship between two variables. The independent variable is set out in the conventional manner on the horizontal x-axis; the frequency is set out on the vertical y-axis. In this way the curve represents y as a function of x.

We must note, then, that a normal distribution is continuous in contrast to a binomial distribution which is discontinuous.

The reader will have noticed that the assumption underlying the game of coin-tossing is that the chances of throwing heads or tails are equal. In other games of chance different conditions obtain. For instance, in dice-throwing the chance of a six, or of any other of the six numbers, is one in six (1 : 6.) We could have approached asymmetrical distributions along these lines. There is no need, however, for our present purpose to consider skew distributions in this manner.

Practical Approximations to the Normal Curve. It used to be thought at one time that (*a*) many distributions found in nature were normal, and that (*b*) there were some special reasons why they should be normal. It is not now thought that the second statement is true. As regards the first statement, all that can be said is that many natural distributions approximate the normal form more or less closely.

Nevertheless, the normal curve plays a very important part in statistical work. On the one hand, it has various well-known mathematical properties, and it is therefore relatively easy to handle. On the other hand, many practical, "bell-shaped" distributions can be treated as if they were normal.

Examples of distributions which are more or less close to normal could be multiplied *ad infinitum*. In the physical sciences we are often confronted with the problem of making a measurement with a rather inadequate measuring instrument. We may develop a more precise tool later, but for the time being the thing to do is to make the same measurement again and again and then regard the mean value of all the measurements as the true one. In such circumstances we find that the individual measurements group themselves in an approximately normal manner about the mean. Thus, we regard each individual measurement as being to a greater or lesser extent in error; therefore, such a distribution is regarded as a distribution of errors.

In the biological sciences we may also deal with near-normal distributions of errors. However, frequently distributions of the qualities themselves, and not only of their measurements, are approximately normal.

In the social sciences too, many distributions are close to

normal. In business, the distributions of garment measurements, e.g., collar sizes, are a good example. Then take psychology: human ability to perform various tasks, as measured on a continuous scale, may be said to be scattered approximately normally. Such variables as examination marks, for instance, have been deliberately normally distributed for reasons of convenience.

There is a useful test—it will be dealt with in a later chapter—whereby it is possible to measure the divergence of a practical distribution from a theoretical, normal one. When this divergence is less than a certain amount, it is then considered to be not significant, and the practical distribution is treated as if it were normal.

However, the greatest importance of the normal curve lies elsewhere. In the next chapter we shall be dealing with the so-called sampling distributions, the consideration of which is crucial in all statistical work. These distributions have been shown to be very nearly normal in certain circumstances. To treat them as normal enables us to make important and easily verifiable statements about the reliability and significance of statistical findings.

Ordinates of the Normal Curve. Consider a theoretical distribution consisting of N cases. Let σ be the standard deviation of the distribution. Let x be the variable expressed in σ-units, so that $x = 0$ at the mean value of the variable, $x = +\sigma$ and $x = -\sigma$ respectively one standard deviation above and below the mean, etc. If the distribution of x is normal, then the frequency represented by the ordinate y varies with x according to the equation

$$ y = \frac{N}{\sigma \sqrt{2\pi}} \, e^{\frac{-x^2}{2\sigma^2}} $$

where e is the base of the Naperian system of logarithms ($e = 2.718$ approx.). The normal curve equation is represented graphically as a function in Fig. 15.

It is clear that the shape of the curve is unaffected by the value of N; a change in N can only shift the ordinates upwards or downwards. But the value of σ does affect the shape of the curve. The greater the σ, the more is the curve spread out. Thus we see that the normal curve equation may be regarded

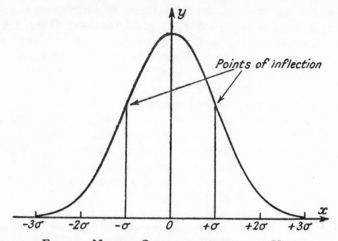

FIG. 15. NORMAL CURVE; x EXPRESSED IN σ UNITS

as representing a family of curves. Three normal curves for a particular value of N, but having three different values of the standard deviation σ, are shown in Fig. 16.

Dealing with a distribution which is normal, or which can reasonably be assumed to be normal, and knowing N, the number of cases, and σ, the standard deviation of the distribution, we are in a position to evaluate from the equation of the curve the ordinate y corresponding to any particular value of the variable. This may be, of course, quite a laborious process, even when the data consist of round figures.

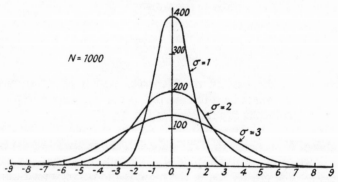

FIG. 16. NORMAL CURVES BASED ON THREE DIFFERENT SIGMAS

For example, let $N = 20{,}000$ and $\sigma = 4$. Suppose, we wish to evaluate y when x is $1 \cdot 2\sigma$. Then, the ordinate is given by

$$y = \frac{20{,}000}{4\sqrt{2\pi}}\, e^{\frac{-(1 \cdot 2 \times 4)^2}{2 \times 4^2}}$$

$$= 970 \text{ (approx.)}$$

To save computational work, it is convenient to use special tables. These have been prepared in such a way that the ordinate corresponding to any value of the variable can be easily obtained. Table XXIV may be used for this purpose. Despite its abbreviated form, this table is quite sufficient for fairly accurate work. Fuller tables will be found in reference books and sets of mathematical tables.

To obtain y corresponding to any value of the variable, we must know the standard deviation σ and the number of cases N in the distribution. Expressing x, as usual, in sigma units, we can easily work out the value of $\dfrac{x}{\sigma}$. We then look up the corresponding value of $e^{\frac{-x^2}{2\sigma^2}}$. Finally, we must multiply this last value by the appropriate value of $\dfrac{N}{\sigma\sqrt{2\pi}}$ to obtain the ordinate y.

Let us return to our example where $N = 20{,}000$ and $\sigma = 4$, and use Table XXIV to obtain the value of y corresponding to $x = 1 \cdot 2\sigma$. We see that when $x = 1 \cdot 2\sigma$, $x/\sigma = 1 \cdot 2$. The value of $e^{\frac{-x^2}{2\sigma^2}}$ corresponding to $1 \cdot 2$ is $0 \cdot 487$. Now this value must be multiplied by the coefficient $N/\sigma\sqrt{2\pi} = 20{,}000/4\sqrt{2\pi}$; the latter works out to be $1{,}990$ (approx.). Hence, the ordinate y corresponding to $x = 1 \cdot 2\sigma$ is given by

$$y = 1{,}990 \times 0 \cdot 487$$

$$\therefore y = 970 \text{ (approx.), as before.}$$

Consider one more example. Given a normal distribution of 10,000 cases, the standard deviation being 5 units, what is the height of the curve representing the distribution 8 units above or below the mean value of the variable?

TABLE XXIV
ORDINATES OF THE NORMAL CURVE

(expressed as fractions of the ordinate $\dfrac{N}{\sigma\sqrt{2\pi}}$, corresponding to $x = 0$)

$\dfrac{x}{\sigma}$	0·00	0·1	0·2	0·3	0·4	0·5	0·6	0·7	0·8	0·9	1·0
$e^{-\frac{x^2}{2\sigma^2}}$	1·000	0·995	0·980	0·956	0·923	0·883	0·835	0·783	0·726	0·667	0·607
$\dfrac{x}{\sigma}$	1·1	1·2	1·3	1·4	1·5	1·6	1·7	1·8	1·9	2·0	2·1
$e^{-\frac{x^2}{2\sigma^2}}$	0·546	0·487	0·430	0·375	0·325	0·278	0·235	0·198	0·164	0·135	0·110
$\dfrac{x}{\sigma}$	2·2	2·3	2·4	2·5	2·6	2·7	2·8	2·9	3·0		
$e^{-\frac{x^2}{2\sigma^2}}$	0·089	0·071	0·56	0·044	0·034	0·026	0·020	0·015	0·011		

When $x = 8$, $x/\sigma = 8/5 = 1·6$. From Table XXIV the corresponding value of $e^{\frac{-x}{2\sigma^2}}$ is 0·278. The coefficient $N/\sigma\sqrt{2\pi} = 10,000/5\sqrt{2\pi}$ works out to be 797.

Hence, $\quad\quad\quad\quad\quad y = 797 \times 0·278$

$\quad\quad\quad\quad\quad\quad \therefore y = 221$ (approx.)

Normal Distribution Constants. As the normal curve is symmetrical about the frequency ordinate corresponding to the mean of the distribution, the mode and the median of the distribution coincide with the mean. The so-called points of

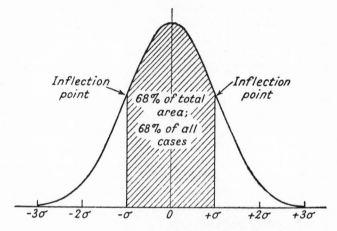

FIG. 17. NORMAL CURVE; AREA CONTAINED BY $\pm\sigma$

inflection of the curve, that is the points where the tangents to the curve cross it, are exactly one standard deviation away from the mean on either side of it, as seen in Fig. 17.

Between minus sigma and plus sigma lie approximately two-thirds of all the cases of a normal distribution. Between -2σ and $+2\sigma$ lie approximately 95 per cent of all the cases. Between -3σ and $+3\sigma$ lie 99·7 per cent of all the cases, and it is therefore reasonable to assume in a practical distribution which is regarded as normal that all the cases lie within plus and minus three standard deviations of the mean.

Thus, given a case which is one of a number of cases normally distributed, there are approximately 68 chances in 100 that it will be no further than $\pm\sigma$ from the mean. Similarly, the chances are 95 in 100 that a case will lie within $\pm 2\sigma$, and the chances are 997 in 1,000 that a case will be within $\pm 3\sigma$ of the mean.

We have seen earlier that in any distribution one-half of all cases lie within the range of plus and minus one probable error (quartile deviation) of the distribution. This, of course, also applies to the normal distribution. Further, it can easily be shown that for a normal distribution $PE = 0.67\sigma$ (approx.), i.e., $\sigma = 1.48\ PE$ (approx.); the relationship between the mean deviation and the standard deviation is: $MD = 0.80\sigma$ (approx.).

Areas under a Normal Curve. If a curve representing any particular normal distribution is plotted, and the whole area under the curve is taken as representing the total number of cases in the distribution, then the area under the curve between any two values of the variable x is proportional to the number of cases which are contained between the two x values. We have seen that 68 per cent of all the cases are found between plus and minus one standard deviation of the mean; it follows, therefore, that 68 per cent of the total area under the normal curve lies between $\pm \sigma$, as shown in Fig. 17.

Tables have been prepared giving percentage areas under the normal curve between the ordinate erected upon the mean value of the variable, $x = 0$, and other ordinates corresponding to different values of x.

Thus, when x is plus or minus infinity, the area to the right (or to the left) of the central ordinate is 50 per cent of the total area. However, since 49.87 per cent of the area lies between the central ordinate and either $+3\sigma$ or -3σ, the area beyond $\pm 3\sigma$ can be in practice regarded as negligible. Approximate percentages of the total area under the normal curve are set out in Table XXV, below; for very accurate work fuller mathematical tables should be used.

EXAMPLE. There are 20,000 cases normally distributed. Using Table XXV, determine how many cases are contained outside $\pm 0.5\sigma$ but inside $\pm 1.5\sigma$.

Percentage of all the cases between $x = 0$ and $x = 1.5\sigma$ is 43.3. Therefore, percentage of all the cases between $\pm 1.5\sigma$ is 86.6. Now there are 19.2 per cent cases between $x = 0$ and $x = 0.5\sigma$, and hence between $\pm 0.5\sigma$ there are 38.4 per cent. Subtracting the inner area from the one bounded by $\pm 1 \cdot 5\sigma$, we have $86 \cdot 6 - 38 \cdot 4$, which equals $48 \cdot 2$ per cent. Since $N = 20,000$, this percentage corresponds to $0 \cdot 482 \times 20,000$, or 9,640 cases.

TABLE XXV

PERCENTAGE AREAS UNDER THE NORMAL CURVE
(areas are bounded by central ordinate and ordinates

corresponding to values of $\frac{x}{\sigma}$)

	$Z = \frac{score\ x}{\sigma}$		0·0	0·1	0·2	0·3	0·4	0·5	0·6	0·7	0·8
	% Area		0·0	4·0	7·9	11·8	15·5	19·2	22·6	25·8	28·8
$\frac{x}{\sigma}$	0·9	1·0	1·1	1·2	1·3	1·4	1·5	1·6	1·7	1·8	1·9
% Area	31·6	34·1	36·4	38·5	40·3	41·9	43·3	44·5	45·5	46·4	47·1
$\frac{x}{\sigma}$	2·0	2·1	2·2	2·3	2·4	2·5	2·6	2·7	2·8	2·9	3·0
% Area	47·7	48·2	48·6	48·9	49·2	49·4	49·5	49·6	49·7	49·8	49·9

CHAPTER VI

Sampling and the Reliability of Estimates

Populations and Samples. It is often the task of a social scientist to examine the nature of the distribution of some variable character in a large population. This entails the determination of values of central tendency and dispersion—usually, the arithmetic mean and the standard deviation. Other features of the distribution, such as its skewness, its peakiness (or the so-called kurtosis), and a measure of its departure from some expected distribution may also be required.

The term *population* is generally used in this connection in a wide but, nevertheless, strict sense. It means the aggregate number of objects or events—not necessarily people—that vary in respect of some character. For example, we may talk about the population of all the school-children of a certain age group in a given area, the botanical population of some particular plant, the population of an industrial product, or even, the hypothetical population of all the possible coin tosses of a certain kind.

Now in practice, the examination of a whole population is often either impossible or impracticable. When this is so, we commonly examine a limited number of individual cases which are a part of the population, that is we examine a *sample* of the population. The various distribution constants of the sample can then be determined, and on this basis the constants of its parent population can be estimated.

Our knowledge of the sample constants can be mathematically precise. On the other hand, we can never know with certainty the constants of the parent population; we can only know what they probably are. Whenever we make an estimate of a population characteristic from a sample, we are faced with the question of the precision of the estimate. Of course, we aim at making our estimates as precise as possible. We shall presently see that the precision of an estimate can be stated in terms of its probability, or more exactly, in terms of the probability of the true value being within such and such a distance of the estimated one.

There are one or two useful terms peculiar to the study of sampling. It will be convenient for the reader to become familiar with them at the outset. Various constants, such as the mean, the standard deviation, etc., which characterise a population are known as *population parameters*. Parameters are the true population measures. They cannot normally be known with certainty. The various measures, such as the mean, the standard deviation, etc., which can be known with certainty are computed from samples. Such measures are known as *sample statistics*. Thus, sample statistics are estimates of population parameters. The precision of the estimates constitutes the so-called *reliability* of the statistics.

Unbiased Sampling. It is useless to determine mathematically the reliability of a sample statistic unless the sample is, to the best of our knowledge, representative of the population from which it is taken, or as we often say, unless it is free from bias. Thus, before attempting to say anything about the reliability of statistics, we must say a word or two about the techniques of forming unbiased samples.

The obvious way of avoiding bias is to form a sample of individuals collected at random, or as it is often put, to take a random sample. Strictly, a sample of the given size is said to be random if the probability of its being chosen is exactly the same as that of any other sample of equal size.

It might be thought that to ensure randomness the individuals of a sample should be collected in what appears to be a haphazard manner. This would be the case if the apparently haphazard choice were truly free of any hidden bias. In practice this condition may not be easily attainable. Examples might be multiplied to show how some sort of unconscious selection creeps into sample formation. The question of how and why sample formation which is intended to be random tends to be biased belongs perhaps properly to the study of psychology rather than to statistics.

In order to ensure that a sample is a random one, i.e., that an equal chance is being given to every individual to be included in the sample, we must use a procedure whereby the choice or rejection of an individual bears no conceivable relation to the character under investigation.

Suppose, for instance, that we wish to gather information about the educational background of the people of some new township. We should have to be careful not to select individuals from certain streets only, or from among those whose names happen to begin with certain letters; for it is conceivable that educational background has had some influence upon the clustering of the inhabitants in some areas, and that people's surnames are in some way characteristic of where they have come from, and hence, possibly, of their education. We must not allow our selection to be influenced by any such factors, even if it does not appear at first sight that our sample is going to be biased. It would be better for the purpose of forming a representative sample of the population, at least as far as the educational background is concerned, to range all the inhabitants in an alphabetical order, and then pick, say, every fiftieth name; for it is indeed difficult to see how a sample so chosen can in any way be influenced by the educational background of the individuals included in it.

Depending upon circumstances, methods other than taking every n^{th} individual can be used to ensure that a sample is randomly chosen. Thus, lottery sampling is another example of a procedure aiming at randomness. If a population is relatively small, every individual can be assigned a ticket, and a proportion of the tickets may then be drawn, say, from a hat. Or, every individual may be assigned a card, and the cards may then be shuffled, and a proportion of the cards, a number required to constitute the sample, can be dealt out in the usual manner.

Sometimes, purposive sampling—paradoxical, as it may at first appear—may be used to produce a sample which represents the population adequately in some one respect. For example, if the sample is to be of necessity very small, and there is a good deal of scatter among the parent population, a purely random sample may by chance yield a mean measure of the variable which is clearly vastly different from the population mean. Provided that we are concerned with the mean only, we may in fact get nearer the truth if we select for our small sample only those individuals that seem on inspection to be close to what appears to be the population average.

However, it is not the purpose of the present book to dwell to any extent upon the methods of ensuring that the observations and experiments of the social sciences conform to certain logical and scientific demands. Assuming that the procedures used are scientifically satisfactory, we wish to see how and when conclusions based on observational and experimental data are statistically, from a mathematical standpoint, warrantable or otherwise. Having emphasised that unbiased sampling is a prerequisite of an adequate statistical treatment, we must begin to discuss the treatment itself.

Sampling Distributions. We have said that the precision of an estimate, or the reliability of a statistic, is stated in terms of the probability of the true value being within a certain distance of the estimated one. We shall now see why and how this is so.

Consider any measure that characterises a population; it may be the mean, the standard deviation, or any other measure. Now suppose that a number of samples are taken from the population. Compute then the particular measure you are considering from each sample. Each sample will yield a slightly different value of the measure. The distribution of such values is known as a *sampling distribution*.

The simplest example of a sampling distribution is a distribution of means of samples. Such sample means are scattered about the true population mean, just as are the individual cases, but of course, the sample means are scattered to a lesser extent. Similarly, sample standard deviations considered together constitute a sampling distribution. Such a distribution is less dispersed than a distribution of individual deviations.

It may be shown that if the distribution of a parent population yields anything like a "bell-shaped" curve, then its sampling distribution—provided the samples are not small —is closer to the normal distribution than the parent distribution itself. Even if a parent distribution is quite far from normal, its sampling distribution, when samples are large, is nearly normal. We may accept therefore that when samples contain more than 50 cases, or even more than 30, and when the distribution curve of the parent population is something like "bell-shaped", then any sampling distribution based on such a population can be regarded for all practical purposes as normal.

However, from what follows the reader will note that it is not generally necessary to assume that a sampling distribution is strictly normal. The only essential assumption is that certain constants of a sampling distribution are the same as those of a corresponding normal distribution. Thus, we take that practically all the sampling distribution is contained within three standard deviations on either side of its mean. But, above all, we assume that 99 per cent of the sample means are contained within ±2·58 standard deviations of the distribution mean, and similarly, that 95 per cent of the sample means are within ±1·96 standard deviations of the distribution mean.

We have just been referring to the standard deviation of a sampling distribution of means, that is to the standard deviation of sample means about the true population mean. This quantity is known as the *standard error of the mean*, and is denoted by the symbol σ_M, or sometimes SE_M.

It has been argued that the term "standard error" is something of a misnomer. This may be so. There may also be a regrettable tendency on the part of students to confuse the standard error with the probable error mentioned earlier. Be this as it may, it should be remembered that the standard error of the mean is simply the standard deviation of a sampling distribution of means.

Confidence Limits of Estimates. To estimate the mean of a population, we take a sample of the population and compute its mean. We then regard it as an estimate of the true population mean. How good is such an estimate?

Our sample mean is only one of many possible sample means. Suppose that the true mean is smaller than our estimated mean. On the assumption that sampling distributions of large samples are approximately normal, our mean will most probably not lie farther than three standard errors above the true mean. Similarly, the chances are very small that the estimated mean will lie farther than three standard errors below the true mean.

We also know that only 5 per cent of the sample means lie outside 1·96 σ_M of the true mean. In other words, the probability of a sample mean being outside ±1·96 σ_M is 0·05. If

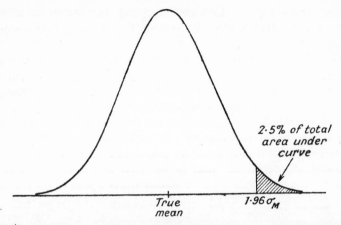

FIG. 18. SAMPLING DISTRIBUTION; TRUE MEAN 1·96σ_M OR MORE
BELOW ESTIMATED MEAN

the true mean is smaller than the estimated one and lies
1·96σ_M or more below it, then our sample mean can only lie
somewhere in the extreme right-hand portion of the distribution shown in Fig. 18. The probability of the true mean
being that far below the estimated mean is, therefore, one-half
of 0·05, or 0·025.

If, on the other hand, the true mean is larger than the
estimated one and lies 1·96σ_M or more above it, then the
estimated mean can only be somewhere in the extreme left-

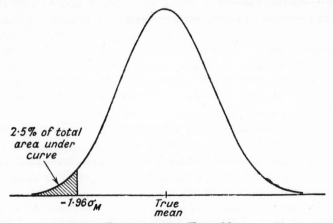

FIG. 19. SAMPLING DISTRIBUTION; TRUE MEAN 1·96σ_M OR MORE
ABOVE ESTIMATED MEAN

hand portion of the distribution of Fig. 19. Therefore, the probability that the true mean lies so far above the estimated mean is again 0·025. Hence, the probability that the true mean lies $1·96\sigma_M$ or more above or below the estimated mean equals 0·025 + 0·025 = 0·05. If P stands for probability, then $P \leqslant$ 0·05 that the true mean is $1·96\sigma_M$ or more away from the estimated mean.

Now the probability of a sample mean being outside $\pm 2·58 \sigma_M$ of the true mean is 0·01. By a reasoning along the lines of the one above we therefore conclude that the probability of a true mean being $2·58\sigma_M$ or more above or below the estimated one is given by $P \leqslant$ 0·01.

We thus see that our estimate of the mean is reliable within certain limits which have been called fiducial or *confidence limits*. On the basis of P = 0·05 (19 in 20 chances of being right), or as we call it, at the 5 per cent level of confidence, the confidence limits lie $1·96\sigma_M$ above and below the estimated mean. Similarly, when P = 0·01, or at the 1 per cent level of confidence, the confidence limits lie $2·58\sigma_M$ above and below the estimated mean.

The farther apart the confidence limits above and below our estimated mean, the greater the probability that the true mean will lie within them. How far apart the confidence limits should be, depends, of course, upon the risk or chance of being wrong which we are prepared to take. In some inquiries the risk of one chance in twenty of making a wrong estimate, that is the 5 per cent level of confidence, is considered acceptable; in others, the risk of only 1 in 50 of being wrong inspires sufficient confidence; and yet in others, the risk of 1 in 100, or the 1 per cent level of confidence, is insisted upon. Generally, in this matter of deciding upon confidence limits much depends also upon the feelings and the temperament of the inquirer.

The Reliability of an Estimated Mean. We have seen that given an agreed risk of being wrong, we can express the reliability of an estimated population mean by stating the confidence limits above and below it. The confidence limits are expressed in terms of the standard error of the mean. The question now arises how to determine the standard error of the mean from one sample only and with no knowledge of the sampling distribution of the population. This can be done quite easily.

First, if σ is the parametric standard deviation of the population, a quantity which cannot be known directly, and N is the number of cases included in the sample, then the standard error of the mean is given by

$$\sigma_M = \frac{\sigma}{\sqrt{N}}$$

While not going into the rigorous proof of this formula, it is easy to see that it complies with our expectations. Obviously, the larger the population sigma, the more scattered will be the sample means, that is the larger must be the sampling distribution sigma which we know by the name of the standard error of the mean. Further, the more cases in the sample, the less scattered will be the sample means; and, conversely, the smaller the samples, the more scattered will be the distribution of the sample means; in fact, it has been shown that σ_M is inversely proportional not just to the number of cases per sample but to the square root of that number.

As it stands, the formula above cannot be of much use, for we do not know the true standard deviation of the population. In order to progress further, we must introduce a crucial assumption, namely that for large N, say above 30, or better above 50 cases, statistics are good approximations of parameters.

We have already seen that the estimated population mean is simply taken to be the sample mean (though we also generally wish to know how confident we should feel about such an estimate, and therefore proceed to determine the estimate's reliability by attaching to it lower and upper limits below and above which it is unlikely that the true mean lies). Now just as the estimated population mean is taken to be the sample mean, so also a good estimate of the standard deviation of a population is given by the standard deviation of a sample of this population. Thus, the population sigma in the formula above may be taken as being approximately equal to the sigma of a sample of this population.

We are now in a position to re-state the formula. If N is the number of cases in a sample, and σ is their standard deviation, then the *standard error of the mean* is given by

$$\sigma_M = \frac{\sigma}{\sqrt{N}}$$

Having calculated the mean, M, and the standard error of the mean, σ_M, from a sample, we can give both the estimate of the population mean and its reliability. Thus at the 5 per cent level the confidence limits are given by $M \pm 1.96 \sigma_M$; and at the 1 per cent level the confidence limits are $M \pm 2.58 \sigma_M$.

Let us illustrate the procedure by a numerical example. Imagine that a socio-economic survey is concerned with the monthly expenditure per family upon a certain group of commodities in a certain area. Suppose that an investigation was carried out upon a random sample of 100 families, and that the sample mean was 30 shillings, the standard deviation having been 5 shillings; round figures are used for simplicity of illustration. What is the reliability of the estimate that the monthly expenditure per family on the commodities in question is 30 shillings?

The standard error of the mean is given by

$$\sigma_M = \sigma / \sqrt{N}$$
$$= 5 / \sqrt{100}$$
$$= 0.5/-$$

Therefore, on the basis of the probability of 0.05 of being incorrect, the upper and lower confidence limits regarding the value of the estimated mean are $30 \pm 1.96 \times 0.5$ shillings. Thus the true mean lies probably ($P = 0.05$) between 29/- and 31/- (approx.).

It should be mentioned that the reliability of a mean may be calculated on the basis of the so-called probable error of the mean instead of the standard error. Further, the reliability of the central tendency measures other than the mean, e.g., of the median, may be established by means of procedures fundamentally similar to the one explained and illustrated above. Our aim here is quite modest; it is to introduce the reader to the principles of reliability determination. Deliberately, only a few selected important statistical measures will be treated.

The Reliability of an Estimated Standard Deviation. We have seen that the standard deviation of a sample is taken as the estimate of the population standard deviation. How reliable is such an estimate? We know how to measure the reliability of an estimated mean. The reliability of an estimated standard deviation is established along similar lines.

If N, the number of individuals in a sample, is large and

certainly not less than about 30, and if σ is the standard deviation obtained from the sample, then a quantity known as *the standard error of the standard deviation*, denoted by σ_σ, is given by

$$\left(\sigma_\sigma = \sigma/\sqrt{2N}\right)$$

We can now reason as before. The probability is 0·05 that the estimated population sigma does not lie outside the limits of $\pm 1·96\sigma_\sigma$. For a higher degree of confidence, viz., for the probability of 0·01 the estimated standard deviation will not lie outside the limits of $\pm 2·58\sigma_\sigma$.

Let us return to the example recently used as an illustration of the reliability of an estimated mean. The data are: $N = 100$, $M = 30/-$ and $\sigma = 5/-$. The standard error of the standard deviation is given by

$$\sigma_\sigma = \sigma/\sqrt{2N}$$
$$= 5/\sqrt{200}$$
$$= 0·355/-$$

Therefore, on the basis of the probability of 0·05 being incorrect, the upper and lower confidence limits regarding the value of the estimated standard deviation are $5 \pm 1·96 \times 0·355$ or $5 \pm 0·7$ shillings. Thus, the standard deviation of the parent population lies probably ($P = 0·05$) between $4s.\ 3\tfrac{1}{2}d.$ and $5s.\ 8\tfrac{1}{2}d.$; or in other words, the standard deviation can be relied upon, at the 5 per cent level of confidence, to be between $4s.\ 3\tfrac{1}{2}d.$ and $5s.\ 8\tfrac{1}{2}d.$

Again, the reliability of other dispersion measures, e.g., of the semi-interquartile range, can be worked out along similar lines. We shall now, however, pass on to another important type of statistic and to the determination of its reliability.

The Significance of Difference between Two Means.
Suppose that we first take one sample of a certain population and find its mean and then do the same for another sample. Even before we have computed the mean of the second sample we know that it will probably be less than $1·96\sigma_M$ away from the first sample mean, the odds being 19 to 1 against. Suppose now that we are not sure whether the second sample has been drawn from the same or another population. If the mean of the second sample is so close to the mean of the first,

sample as to be within the range of high probability of the true mean of the population from which the first sample was drawn, then we conclude that the second sample may have been drawn from the same population. But if the mean of the second sample falls beyond the range within which the first sample's parent population mean probably lies, then we can only conclude that the second sample was probably drawn from a different population.

The problem above is known as the problem of significance of the difference between two means. It is a highly practical problem. Suppose we were to conduct a socio-psychological inquiry to answer the question whether there is a real difference in verbal facility between town and country school-children in a certain area. In the language of statistics, we should say that we wish to know whether from the point of view of verbal facility town and country children can or cannot be treated as one population. Assuming that we have suitable tests and reasonably large unbiased samples of school-children from the urban and rural areas, we proceed to obtain the scores of individual children.

Having computed the mean scores for our two samples, and assuming that the two means differ, we are now faced with the question: "is the difference significant?" For even if we drew two samples of urban school-children, their means would probably differ somewhat; and there would also be a difference between the mean scores of two samples of rural children. So it is clear that the difference between the mean scores of samples of children from urban and rural areas must be greater than a certain amount before we can feel confident that there is most probably a difference between the verbal facility of town and of country school-children in the area.

Once again we can feel confident that the difference between two means is most probably not due to chance fluctuation of samples, i.e., that the difference is significant, if it is at least 1·96 its standard error at the 5 per cent level of confidence, or at least 2·58 its standard error at the 1 per cent level of confidence. We, therefore, must be able to compute the *standard error of the difference between two means.* We must here add a word of warning. We are considering means of uncorrelated measures. The subject of correlation is dealt with in Chapters IX and X. The computation of the standard error of the difference between two means of correlated measures will be found in the last section of Chapter IX. At this stage we are dealing with the standard error of the difference between two independent (or uncorrelated) means. It is denoted by σ_D and is given by

$$\sigma_D = \sqrt{\sigma_{M_1}^2 + \sigma_{M_2}^2}$$

where σ_{M_1} is the standard error of the mean for the first sample, and σ_{M_2} is the standard error of the mean for the second sample.

We already know that $\sigma_M = \sigma/\sqrt{N}$. Therefore, for the first sample:

$$\sigma_{M_1} = \sigma_1/\sqrt{N_1}, \text{ and hence } \sigma_{M_1}^2 = \sigma_1^2/N_1,$$

and for the second sample:

$$\sigma_{M_2} = \sigma_2/\sqrt{N_2}, \text{ and hence } \sigma_{M_2}^2 = \sigma_2^2/N_2$$

Thus, the standard error of the difference between two means may be expressed in terms of

σ_1 — standard deviation of first sample,
σ_2 — standard deviation of second sample,
N_1 — number of individuals in first sample,
N_2 — number of individuals in second sample;

$$\sigma_D = \sqrt{(\sigma_1^2/N_1 + \sigma_2^2/N_2)}$$

Denote the means of the first and second samples respectively by M_1 and M_2. The difference between these means divided by σ_D is known as the "critical ratio",

$$CR = (M_1 - M_2)/\sigma_D \text{ or } CR = (M_2 - M_1)/\sigma_D$$

If the critical ratio is equal to or greater than $1\cdot96$, then the probability is $0\cdot05$ that the two samples are drawn from the same population. Similarly, if CR is equal to or greater than $2\cdot58$, the probability is $0\cdot01$ that the samples belong to the same population. Using the standard phraseology, we say that a difference is significant at the 5 per cent level if $CR \geqslant 1\cdot96$, or is significant at the 1 per cent level if $CR \geqslant 2\cdot58$.

Consider now an example from the field of occupational psychology. A certain test of manual dexterity is given to two samples of 100 individuals randomly selected from two different occupational fields. Suppose the mean score for the first occupation is 84, the standard deviation being 7, and the mean score for the second occupation is 88, the standard deviation being 6. Are the populations of the two occupations significantly different as regards manual dexterity?

The standard error of the difference between the means is given by

$$
\begin{aligned}
\sigma_D &= \sqrt{(\sigma_1{}^2/N_1 + \sigma_2{}^2/N_2)} \\
&= \sqrt{(7^2/100 + 6^2/100)} \\
&= 0.92 \text{ (approx.)}
\end{aligned}
$$

The critical ratio,

$$
\begin{aligned}
(M_2 - M_1)/\sigma_D &= (88-84)/0.9 \\
\therefore CR &= 4.45
\end{aligned}
$$

$CR = 4.45$ is much greater than either 1.96 or 2.58. Thus the difference between the manual dexterity scores of the two populations must be considered highly significant or highly reliable.

Just as we can judge the significance of difference between sample means, so also is it possible to determine the significance of difference between two standard deviations. The reader will find this and other techniques discussed in those reference text-books which are designed to cover fully the procedures concerned with the reliability of statistics. Having worked through this chapter and understood the principles underlying the determination of statistical significance, the student will experience no difficulty in dealing with other types of problems which involve the computation of standard errors and reliability.

CHAPTER VII

The Reliability of Small-sample Statistics

Large and Small Samples. So far we have dealt with the methods of determining the reliability of statistics applicable only to what we have called large samples, and the reader's attention has repeatedly been drawn to this limitation. Now the smaller the samples, the more inaccurate become these methods.

When N, the number of individuals per sample, is less than, say, 50, then it is better to determine the reliability of sample statistics by means other than those discussed in the last chapter. This becomes imperative when N is less than, say, 30; otherwise the errors introduced, if the ordinary large-sample methods are employed, will be very considerable. In this chapter we shall, therefore, deal with the special methods used in small-sample work.

It will be seen that the methods used for the calculation of the reliability of statistics obtained from small samples may be equally well applied to large samples. However, the extra accuracy thus achieved does not warrant the additional work which would be entailed.

The Parametric Standard Deviation. In the treatment of large samples we have been assuming that the sample standard deviation is a good estimate of the population or parametric standard deviation. As a matter of fact we have consistently been slightly underestimating the population sigma in this way. The error involved becomes considerable only when N is small.

The Standard Error of a Mean. To compensate for the fact that the sample sigma underestimates the population sigma, a modified standard error formula must be used. If σ is the sample standard deviation, and N is the number of individual cases per sample, then for small samples the standard error of a mean, σ_M, is given by

$$\sigma_M = \sigma/\sqrt{(N-1)}$$

It will be noted that when N is large the difference between $\sqrt{N-1}$ and $\sqrt{N}$ is small compared with the value of $\sqrt{N}$, and consequently the standard error of the mean is given by

$$\sigma_M = \sigma/\sqrt{N} \text{ (approx.)}$$

Some Initial Assumptions. In large-sample work we had no need to make any assumptions about the nature of the distribution of the parent population. Further, we said that provided the distribution curve of the parent population was anything like bell-shaped, its sampling distribution could reasonably be assumed to be normal. We then based our work on this assumption of normality of sampling distributions.

Now in small-sample work we are obliged at the start to assume that the parent population distributions are normal; we have already said that, in any case, such an assumption is often fully justifiable. However, despite this initial assumption, we cannot also assume that sampling distributions, if the samples taken are small, are normal. In fact, the crucial difference between large-sample and small-sample work is associated with the different natures of sampling distributions obtained from large and from small samples.

We have said that a sampling distribution based on small samples, i.e., a distribution of small-sample means, cannot be regarded as approximately normal. Such a sampling distribution is still represented by a bell-shaped curve, but the shape of the curve departs more and more from normality as N, the number of cases per sample, decreases.

The Nature of Sampling Distributions. In consequence of the fact that in small-sample work no initial assumption regarding the normality of a sampling distribution can be made, the probability of divergence of a sample mean from the true population mean must be computed not from a normal sampling distribution curve but from a curve appropriate to the value of N, the number of cases in the sample.

We have seen that on the assumption of a normal sampling distribution—an assumption which is warrantable when N is large—the probability that the true population mean lies outside $\pm 1 \cdot 96 \, \sigma_M$ of the estimated mean is equal to 0·05. This is strictly true only when N is infinitely large, which is an unattainable condition.

When the number of cases per sample is 50, the probability that the true mean lies as far as or further than $1 \cdot 96 \sigma_M$ away from the estimated mean is somewhat more than 0·05. In other words, at N equal to 50 the fiducial limits above and below the estimated mean, at the 5 per cent level of confidence, are somewhat above $\pm 1 \cdot 96 \sigma_M$.

Now in fact, for the probability of 0·05 of one's estimate being incorrect, i.e., at the 5 per cent level of confidence, the fiducial limits are $2 \cdot 01 \, \sigma_M$ above and below the estimated mean instead of $1 \cdot 96 \sigma_M$. When $N = 30$, for the probability of 0·05 of one's estimate being incorrect, the confidence limits are $2 \cdot 04 \, \sigma_M$ above and below the estimated mean. When $N = 10$, for the same probability of being wrong, the confidence limits are $2 \cdot 26 \, \sigma_M$ on either side of the estimated mean.

The sampling distributions corresponding to different values of N are known as "Student's" t-distributions. The so-called t-values are the distances from the mean value which correspond to different levels of confidence. When N, the number of cases per sample, is very large, then the t-values corresponding to the 5 per cent and 1 per cent levels of confidence are, as we have seen before, $1 \cdot 96$ and $2 \cdot 58$ respectively, the t-distribution being then taken to be normal. The lower the values of N, the higher are the t-values for the same levels of confidence. It is clear that t-distribution curves are symmetrical about the mean; they are bell-shaped like the normal curve, but are more peaky and have longer "tails" than the latter.

For the present purpose we need not concern ourselves with the t-distances from the mean which correspond to many different P-values representing confidence levels. It will be sufficient to know and it will make the presentation simpler if t-values corresponding only to $P = 0 \cdot 05$ and $P = 0 \cdot 01$ are considered.

For reasons which need not be discussed here, we do not commonly set out t-values against N, the number of cases per sample, as might be expected. Instead, t-values are set out against the quantity $(N - 1)$, the number of degrees of freedom.

A series of *t*-values which correspond to a number of selected values of degrees of freedom for the two usually required levels of confidence or significance are given in Table XXVI.

TABLE XXVI

SELECTED *t*-VALUES AT THE 5% AND 1% LEVELS OF SIGNIFICANCE

Degrees of Freedom $(N - 1)$	*t*-values	
	at $P = 0.05$	at $P = 0.01$
1,000	1·96	2·58
100	1·98	2·63
50	2·01	2·68
40	2·02	2·71
30	2·04	2·75
25	2·06	2·79
20	2·09	2·84
15	2·13	2·95
10	2·23	3·17
9	2·26	3·25
8	2·31	3·36
7	2·36	3·50
6	2·45	3·71
5	2·57	4·03

The Reliability of a Mean estimated from a Small Sample. To determine the reliability of an estimated mean we must first compute the standard error of the mean. It must be remembered that the formula appropriate for small samples given earlier in this chapter should be used. Then, instead of multiplying the standard error by the coefficients of 1·96 and 2·58 (obtained from the normal curve) in order to establish confidence limits for the 5 per cent and the 1 per cent levels of confidence respectively, we are now obliged to use an appropriate t-distribution curve to obtain correct coefficient values.

The determination of the reliability of an estimated mean, when the estimate is based on a small sample, may be best illustrated by means of a numerical example. Suppose that eight tests were made upon a certain type of wire, and it was found that the mean breaking strength for the eight tests was 243 lb. and the standard deviation 7·61 lb. How reliable at the 1 per cent level of confidence is the estimate that the breaking strength of the wire is 243 lb.?

Using the standard-error-of-a-mean formula appropriate for small samples, we have

$$\left(\begin{array}{l} \sigma_M = \sigma/\sqrt{(N-1)} \\ \sigma_M = 7\cdot61/\sqrt{7} \\ = 2\cdot88 \text{ lb.} \end{array}\right)$$

At eight tests there are seven degrees of freedom. From Table XXVI the t-value corresponding to $(N-1) = 7$ at $P = 0\cdot01$ is 3·50. Therefore, at the 1 per cent level of confidence our limits are given by $243 \pm 3\cdot50 \times 2\cdot88 = 243 \pm 10\cdot1$ lb. (approx.). This means that there are 99 chances in 100 that the true average breaking strength of the wire is somewhere between 232·9 lb. and 253·1 lb.

The Reliability of Scatter Values. As with large samples, the first step towards the determination of the reliability of a measure of dispersion obtained from a sample is to compute the standard error of the measure. The measure of dispersion most frequently used is the standard deviation. We shall now see how to determine the reliability of a standard deviation obtained from a small sample.

We saw in the last chapter that the standard error of a standard deviation, denoted by σ_σ, is given by

$$\sigma_\sigma = \sigma/\sqrt{2N}$$

where σ is the sample standard deviation, and N is the number of cases in the sample.

However, we have noted earlier in this chapter that the sample standard deviation tends to be less than the parametric standard deviation, particularly if the standard deviation is obtained from a small sample. We have already seen that for this reason the formula for the standard error of the mean for small-sample work has had to be modified. Analogously, the standard error of the standard deviation for small values of N is given more accurately by

$$\sigma_\sigma = \sigma/\sqrt{2(N-1)}$$

Having calculated the standard error of the standard deviation, we may now determine the reliability of a standard deviation obtained from a sample. Instead of basing our confidence limits for a given confidence level on the normal distribution curve we now base them on an appropriate t-distribution curve. To illustrate the method we may conveniently refer to the example just used in connection with the evaluation of the reliability of an estimated mean.

In this case there were eight tests ($N = 8$); the mean was found to 243 lb. and the standard deviation 7·61 lb. The standard error of the standard deviation is therefore

$$
\begin{aligned}
\sigma_\sigma &= \sigma/\sqrt{2(N-1)} \\
&= 7{\cdot}61/\sqrt{2 \times 7} \\
&= 2{\cdot}04 \text{ lb.}
\end{aligned}
$$

Now with eight tests there are seven degrees of freedom. We see from Table XXVI that when $P = 0{\cdot}01$, the t-value corresponding to $(N - 1) = 7$ is 3·50. Therefore, at the 1 per cent level of confidence our limits are given by 7·61 $\pm$ 3·50 $\times$ 2·04, or 7·61 $\pm$ 7·11 (approx.). This means that if we took a very large number of readings, the chances are 99 in 100 that the standard deviation (representing the measure of scatter of the readings) could be anywhere between 0·50 lb. and 14·72 lb.

The reader will appreciate that the reliability of other measures of central tendency and dispersion obtained from small samples may also be established.

Methods of Establishing the Significance of Difference between Means. As in the last chapter, we shall be dealing only with sample means of variables which are independent of or uncorrelated with one another. The strict meaning of correlation and the method of finding out whether or not there is a significant correlation between two variables will be dealt with in a later chapter.

We have seen that with large samples, the difference between two sample means is regarded as significant at the 5 per cent level of confidence when it is greater than $1 \cdot 96$ times its standard error; it is significant at the 1 per cent level of confidence when it is greater than $2 \cdot 58$ its standard error. The coefficients by which the standard error is multiplied, the so-called critical ratios or CR-values, are based upon the normal curve, as it is assumed that sampling distributions for large samples are normal.

Now we already know that we base statements regarding reliability and significance in small-sample work not upon normal but upon t-distribution curves. The appropriate t-distribution curve is determined by the total number of degrees of freedom for the two samples. If N_1 is the number of cases in the first sample and N_2 the number of cases in the second sample, then the total number of degrees of freedom is $(N_1 - 1) + (N_2 - 1)$.

Consider a numerical example. A group of mental hospital patients were given a test designed to confirm a differentation between certain cases of depression and schizophrenia. Seventeen diagnosed depressive and eleven schizophrenic cases were used; the mean score of the former was 66 and for the latter was 75; the standard deviations were 8 and 9 respectively. The two groups were matched as nearly as possible for age, sex, general intelligence and social background. From the results as presented, can it be concluded that schizophrenic patients score significantly less than depressive ones?

The standard error of the difference between means is given by

$$\sigma_D = \sqrt{\sigma_{M_1}{}^2 + \sigma_{M_2}{}^2}$$

where σ_{M_1} is the standard error of the mean for the first sample, and σ_{M_2} is the standard error of the mean for the second sample.

It is important to remember here that for small samples

and
$$\sigma_{M_1} = \sigma_1/\sqrt{(N_1 - 1)}$$

$$\sigma_{M_2} = \sigma_2/\sqrt{N_2 - 1)}$$

where σ_1 and σ_2 are the standard deviations of the first and second samples and N_1 and N_2 are the numbers of cases in the first and second samples respectively.

In our example
$$\sigma_{M_1} = 8/\sqrt{(17 - 1)}$$
$$= 2 \cdot 00$$
$$\sigma_{M_2} = 9/\sqrt{(11 - 1)}$$
$$= 2 \cdot 85$$

Thus, substituting into the formula for the standard error, we have
$$\sigma_D = \sqrt{2 \cdot 00^2 + 2 \cdot 85^2}$$
$$= 3 \cdot 48$$

The critical ratio is given by
$$CR = (M_1 - M_2)/\sigma_D \text{ or } CR = (M_2 - M_1)/\sigma_D$$

In our example
$$CR = (75 - 66)/3 \cdot 48$$
$$= 2 \cdot 59$$

The number of degrees of freedom is
$$df = (N_1 - 1) + (N_2 - 1)$$
$$= 26$$

We may now use Table XXVI. We see that our difference between mean test scores is significant at the 5 per cent level of confidence; it is, however, not significant at the 1 per cent level.

We may conclude that it would be desirable to state with greater confidence that on the whole depressive patients score less than the schizophrenic ones. To be able to do so we must use more patients in our inquiry. If we still obtain a difference between means of the same order as before, then, clearly, with larger number of cases, we can place rather greater reliance upon the difference such as it is.

Sometimes only raw scores for two samples may be available, and it has not otherwise already been necessary to work out the two standard deviations. In such circumstances another formula for the standard error of the difference between two means may be used. The formula referred to here is not strictly equivalent to the general formula given earlier in this chapter; however, it is no less accurate. It is, perhaps, best for beginners not to depart, whenever possible, from the general method explained earlier.

Now before this special formula for the standard error of the difference between two means can be applied, the means for the two samples must be worked out. Then all the deviations from the mean of each sample must be obtained. Then, if

x_1-values are the deviations from the first mean, and

x_2-values are the deviations from the second mean,

the standard error of the difference between the two means is given by

$$S_D = \sqrt{\frac{\Sigma x_1{}^2 + \Sigma x_2{}^2}{(N_1 - 1) + (N_2 - 1)} \times \left(\frac{1}{N_1} + \frac{1}{N_2}\right)}$$

where N_1 is the number of cases in the first sample, and

N_2 is the number of cases in the second sample.

Having obtained the value of the standard error by this method, the significance of a difference between two means is established in the usual manner. Table XXVI should be used to obtain t-values corresponding to the appropriate number of degrees of freedom and the required level of confidence (i.e., either $P = 0.05$ or $P = 0.01$).

CHAPTER VIII

Statistical Significance and the Testing of Hypotheses

The Methods of the Social Sciences. It may be maintained that the task of a science is to explain the phenomena which lie in the sphere of its interest. An explanation may start with a guess. But how are we to know whether a particular guess is right or wrong? We must test it against observed facts in such a way as to gain independent evidence in favour of the guessed explanation.

If a guess is not, on the face of it, a wild one, then it is known as an hypothesis. It may be maintained that, on analysis, all that scientists do is test hypotheses, which is only another way of saying that all the activities of scientists are subordinated towards explaining observed phenomena. Observation itself is selective and must be relevant to some underlying expectation, hypothesis or theory.

In the testing of hypotheses we may or we may not employ precise measurement and/or mathematics. Sometimes we simply resort to checking up gross facts. Darwin, for instance, made a series of "historical hypotheses" about the ancestry of man. This was, in part, in order to explain the similarity in the physical structure between man and other animals. From such hypotheses two things followed: first, certain other, as yet unknown, similarities would have to exist; second, a series of links between man and his ancestors should be discoverable. The tests of Darwin's hypotheses lay in obtaining positive evidence of both kinds. As is well known, more and more independent evidence in favour of Darwin's hypotheses is still being accumulated, and we feel more and more confident that Darwin must have been right.

On the other hand, turning to fact for confirmation or falsification of a theory may involve a good deal of precise measurement. To explain why the orbit of a certain planet was as it was found to be, it seemed necessary to suppose the existence of a new planet. One way of testing such a hypothesis would have been to use, if possible, more powerful telescopes to see if the supposed planet in fact existed. Alternatively, certain deductions and calculations based on the initial hypothesis could have been made regarding the behaviour of certain other celestial bodies, and then crucial and precise observations of their behaviour would have constituted a satisfactory test of the initial hypothesis.

This last procedure is as often as not the usual procedure of the physical sciences. A series of calculations lead to crucial, carefully carried-out measurements; and the results of the measurements decide whether a hypothesis stands or falls. Often there are no two ways about it; we are either right or wrong. This, unfortunately, can only rather infrequently be applied to the social sciences. That is why there is sometimes some doubt expressed as to whether the social sciences are sciences at all. But to deny on these grounds that the social sciences are sciences amounts to asserting that the characteristic of a science is precision. Such a position is difficult to maintain. If, on the other hand, we hold that a scientific procedure is essentially characterised by a search of general explanations and the testing of hypotheses, then disciplines such as economics, sociology and psychology admit of being scientific.

In the social sciences an answer to a question often appears ambiguous. Do, for instance, certain kinds of children do badly at school because they simply lack the necessary intellectual ability, or may there be other reasons? Let our first hypothesis be that they do lack the aptitude. We then test a sample of the children in question as best as we can for intellectual aptitude and compare them with other children. Suppose that our tests reveal that the individuals in our sample of the children who show lack of scholastic success lack somewhat in aptitude as compared with some standard (control group). Can we feel confident that there is a real lack of aptitude among the children under investigation, and that the obtained results cannot have, quite likely, been due to chance? The answer to this question turns on establishing the reliability of a statistic.

It is a fact that in the social sciences tests of hypotheses often do not yield mathematically clear-cut answers. They are often answers which may or may not have statistical significance. And we have already seen that the concept of statistical significance is rooted in probability.

Null Hypotheses. While dealing with questions the answers to which may depend upon statistical significance, it is not inconvenient to talk about testing null hypotheses. A null hypothesis is simply one which asserts that in a given situation nothing but the laws of chance are operative. Thus, a null hypothesis is an assumption that a given set of statistical data can be entirely explained or accounted for by probability alone.

It is, of course, not necessary to talk about testing null hypotheses while being concerned with tests of probability and significance. It would appear that the popularity of this phraseology is associated with the awareness among the social scientists that, on analysis, any scientific work consists in essence of the testing of hypotheses.

This chapter will be concerned with various statistical procedures which can be regarded as aiming directly at testing null hypotheses. The reader will already be familiar with some of these, though he has not looked at them from quite this angle. The procedures may be grouped into several categories, of which we shall only treat a selected few.

Significance of Difference between Means. To test a difference between two sample means for significance amounts to the testing of a null hypothesis. The null hypothesis would here assert that no true difference exists between two sample means, i.e., it would assert that two samples are drawn from the same population and therefore the difference between their means, such as it is, is associated with the normal scatter of sample means.

By comparing the obtained difference between means with its standard error in the manner explained in the last two chapters, we put the null hypothesis to test. A measure of confirmation of the hypothesis is achieved if it is shown that the difference is not significant, even at the 5 per cent level of confidence. The hypothesis is falsified if the difference between the two means is shown to be unlikely to be due to sheer sampling error, i.e., if the difference is significant at, say, the 5 per cent, or better, the 1 per cent level of confidence.

Expectation of Binomial Distribution. We often deal with distributions of a single quality or attribute. In a number of cases examined it is either present or absent; or, as we often put it, it either succeeds or fails to appear. Suppose we toss a single coin. We can expect with an ordinary coin that there will be equal proportions of heads and tails when the number of throws has been reasonably large. That is, the coin when flipped will come up heads as often as tails. Or, as the statistician would say, heads will succeed as often as will fail to make an appearance, and the same can be said about tails.

Suppose now that we are not sure whether a coin is symmetrical. We may carry out an experiment, postulating a null hypothesis, that is postulating perfect symmetry. If we then toss the coin, say, twelve times, we may expect that heads will probably appear six times. The question now arises what must be the proportion of heads to tails in order that we may regard the null hypothesis as falsified.

Problems of this kind arise again and again. We may consider the method of answering them with the help of a more practical example. We may use one from the field of the psychology of perception. Suppose that we wish to know whether a partially colour-blind Subject is capable of distinguishing between two hues which we have reason to believe are close to his sensory threshold of colour discrimination. Suppose that we carry out an experiment where the pair of colours placed side by side are presented to the Subject, say, twelve times. We must assume, of course, that the experiment is intelligently designed; we should expect the colours to be matched as regards brightness and saturation, and other sources of error to be eliminated or balanced.

Now if the Subject cannot really distinguish between the hues, he will be as likely to be correct as incorrect in naming them each time they are shown to him. In other words, the chances of an apparent success in telling which colour is which will then equal the chances of failure. How far must the actual proportion of successes and failures diverge from equality to be regarded as not accidental, that is how unequal must be the numbers of successes and failures before we can regard the null hypothesis postulating the Subject's inability truly to perceive the difference as falsified?

To answer this question recall the binomial expansions

dealt with in Chapter V. As the Subject makes 12 attempts and each time is either right or wrong, to determine the probability of any number of successes we must consider the expansion of $(1 + 1)^{12}$:

$(1 + 1)^{12} = 1 + 12 + 66 + 220 + 495 + 792 +$
$924 + 792 + 495 + 220 + 66 + 12 + 1 = 4,096$

On the assumption of the null hypothesis, that is assuming that the Subject is unable truly to distinguish between the two colours, the probability of 12 successes is 1/4096. The probability of 11 or more successes is $(1 + 12)/4096$ or 13/4096. The probability of 10 or more successes is given by $(1 + 12 + 66)/4096$ or 79/4096, and so on.

Now assuming that the Subject is unable to distinguish between the two colours, we must decide how improbable the Subject's degree of success must be before our confidence in the initial assumption is destroyed. It is customary—as we have seen earlier—to be fully satisfied with the 1 per cent level of confidence, and certainly with not less than the 5 per cent level. Accordingly we may regard the null hypothesis as falsified or at least highly suspect if the Subject's degree of success is greater than can be expected at the 5 per cent level of confidence.

At this agreed level, the probability of success is no more than 5 in 100, which works out to be 204·8/4096. We see, then, that at the 5 per cent level of confidence 10 successes are still significantly more than can occur by chance. On the other hand, the probability of 9 successes in 12 trials is given by $(1 + 12 + 66 + 220)/4096 = 299/4096$. Thus we see that if the Subject were successful 9 times out of 12, we could not regard this as a reliable evidence that he or she can distinguish between the two colours and that the answers are obtained other than by guessing.

Suppose now that the pair of colours were presented to the Subject only 6 times instead of 12, and suppose further that the Subject was successful in distinguishing between them 5 times. Can this be regarded as a falsification of the null hypothesis?

We note that $(1 + 1)^6 = 1 + 6 + 15 + 20 + 15 + 6 + 1 = 64$. First consider the probability of 4 or more correct guesses. It is given by $(1 + 6 + 15)/64 = 22/64$, which is over 34 per cent. Obviously, four correct answers could not at all be regarded as indicative of the Subject's ability to distinguish the colours. Now, had the Subject been successful 5 times out of 6, the probability that the null hypothesis is true or that the Subject is merely guessing would be given by $(1 + 6)/64 = 7/64$. Thus, 5 successes in 6 trials still do not significantly differ from a chance result at the 5 per cent level of confidence.

It is clear, in fact, that only if the Subject had been successful in every one of the 6 trials, would the null hypothesis have been refuted at the 5 per cent level of confidence, for then the probability of success by sheer chance would have been $1/64$. However, at the 1 per cent level of confidence such a result would still not have been significant.

Thus, if we felt confident of the Subject's ability to distinguish between two colours only when the experimental results were proved significant at the 1 per cent level of confidence, we should have had to give the Subject at least 7 trials. On the assumption of the null hypothesis, the probability of success in every one of the 7 attempts would be 1 in 128, that is would be less than 0·01. Therefore, a falsification of the null hypothesis of the 1 per cent level of confidence would require (a) at least 7 trials, and (b) 7 successes in the 7 trials.

Checking Obtained Results against Normal Curve Probabilities. We have just been comparing observed and probable proportions of presences and absences or successes and failures, where the number of observations is quite small. We have been using binomial expansions of $(1 + 1)^n$, where n corresponds to the number of observations. When n becomes large, say 50 or 100, the work involved in computing the binomial expansion terms becomes very considerable.

However, we already know that when n is large, the binomial point curve approximates closely the normal curve. Therefore, we can compare obtained results directly with the probabilities calculated from the normal curve, as set out in Table XXV.

Suppose that a test containing 64 items is given to entrants into a certain occupation with a view to testing their knowledge of some particular subject. Suppose that the test is simply constructed, each item consisting of two statements one of which is true and the other false. The task of the person sitting the examination is to underline the true statement.

Now by sheer chance anyone can be as often right as wrong.

Then, how many more than 32 correct answers indicate that the examinee has some knowledge of the subject and is not merely guessing? In other words, we have to answer the question: "What must be the examinee's score to falsify a null hypothesis?"

Clearly, if we gave the test to a large number of people all of whom merely guess the correct answers or pick them out at random, then many of them would be 32 times right and 32 times wrong. Others, however, would be 33 times right and 31 times wrong, or 31 times right and 33 times wrong.

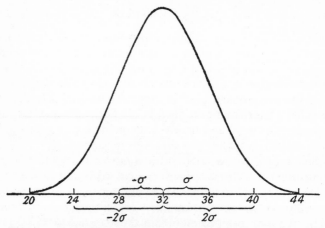

FIG. 20. PROBABILITY DISTRIBUTION OF SUCCESSFUL GUESSES
Questionnaire contains 64 true-false items

Some others, somewhat fewer in number, would be 34 times right and 30 times wrong, or 30 times right and 34 times wrong, and so on. There would be very few indeed, if any, who would be right or wrong on all the 64 occasions.

Such successes, as also such failures, would be distributed in the manner shown in Fig. 20, where the vertical co-ordinates represent the frequencies corresponding to various possible proportions of successes to failures. The mode of the probability curve would correspond to 32 successes (and 32 failures). Compared with the mode frequency, there would be negligibly few successes with all the 64 test items or with none of them.

The standard deviation of this curve is given by the formula

$$\sigma = \sqrt{npq}$$

where n is the number of test items [or in general the index of the $(p + q)^n$ expansion], and p and q are the probabilities of successes and failures.

In our example n equals 64, while p and q are equal to $\frac{1}{2}$, $(p + q)$ being unity. It should be appreciated that p and q may have other values. Had there been, for instance, four statements per item and only one of them correct, the probability of success would have been $\frac{1}{4}$ and the probability of failure would have been equal to $\frac{3}{4}$.

In our example, then, the standard deviation of the distribution is given by

$$\sigma = \sqrt{64 \times \tfrac{1}{2} \times \tfrac{1}{2}}$$

that is, $\sigma = 4$

We know that in a normal distribution 95 times out of 100 a case (here a proportion of successes to failures) lies within $\pm 1.96\sigma$. Thus, the probability is 0.05 that the number of successes will be greater or less than $32 \pm 2 \times 4$ (approx.), that is greater than 40 or less than 24.

Thus, only if an examinee gives at least 40 correct answers can we feel confident (at the 5 per cent level of significance) that he or she has not been guessing and has, in fact, some knowledge of the subject.

The problem just considered must be regarded as a very simple example of checking obtained results against normal curve probabilities. We cannot deal here with more complex problems of this kind. Instead, we shall now concern ourselves with yet another statistical technique which may be looked upon as being directed towards the testing of null hypotheses.

The Statistic of χ^2 (Chi-Squared). A problem which may sometimes arise is whether an observed frequency distribution of a variable conforms to some expectation. If the expected distribution is regarded as a null hypothesis, we may wish to know what is the standing of the hypothesis in the light of the evidence of observation.

We take a sample; its observed distribution is one of many which could be obtained from other samples. Now the divergence between an expected distribution of a variable and one actually obtained may be expressed in terms of a quantity called χ^2 (chi-squared). From this and some additional knowledge, as explained later, we may tell what is the probability that the difference between the observed and the theoretical results is due to chance sampling fluctuations.

The formula by which to compute χ^2 is

$$\chi^2 = \Sigma[(O - E)^2/E]$$

where O is the observed frequency of the variable, and E is the expected frequency; Σ is "the sum of".

Now sometimes there are only a few values of O and E given; sometimes we compare two continuous curves and must decide how many pairs of O and E to consider. Broadly, the more pairs are taken the higher will be the value of χ^2 at which we shall arrive. Therefore, to decide whether a value of χ^2 is indicative of a significant divergence of the observation from expectation, we must also take into account the number of degrees of freedom on which the particular computation of the χ^2 is based. We have seen earlier how to determine the number of degrees of freedom (df) in a somewhat special case; in connection with some practical examples we shall see how to arrive at df-values in other cases.

Having determined χ^2 and df we are in a position to look up a table (such as Table XXXII) which gives the probability of the observed divergence on the assumption of a null hypothesis. It will be seen that various types of problems demand slightly different treatments. Let us, therefore, go on with the discussion of the χ^2-test by reference to several examples.

Chi-Squared and Tests of Independence. It is frequently necessary to ascertain whether a set of obtained data indicates that two variables are related. For instance, we may be confronted with a set of figures showing the number of births month by month in a particular country in a certain year. There is some fluctuation in the number of births from month to month, and we may wish to know whether the fluctuation can on the whole be regarded as seasonal. We are not so much interested in a coefficient of correlation between the variables of time and number of births, as in confirming or refuting the null hypothesis that the variables are independent of one another.

The χ^2-test will tell us in a case of this kind whether there is reason to believe that there is some relationship between the variables. The degree of relationship is not indicated by the test. If correlation coefficients for two pairs of variables are given, then the larger coefficient would indicate a closer relationship. But the χ^2-test of two such relationships would not tell us which relationship is the closer; it would tell us in which case we may feel more confident that there is some relationship.

Consider a practical numerical example. A set of 50 Science examination papers has been marked, and each paper has been assigned to one of the four categories A, B, C and D. A set of English papers by the same 50 pupils has been similarly marked. We may wish to know whether successes in Science and in English should be regarded as related or as independent of each other.

Suppose that the examination results were as set out in Table XXVII. Each pupil may have obtained one of the sixteen different pairs of marks, AA, AB, etc., down to DD. The number of cases which fall in every one of the sixteen arrangements is shown in the appropriate cell.

TABLE XXVII

EXAMINATION RESULTS OF FIFTY PUPILS
IN ENGLISH AND SCIENCE

SCIENCE

		A	B	C	D	Totals
	A	2	3	3	0	8
ENGLISH	B	2	7	7	0	16
	C	2	5	8	3	18
	D	0	2	4	2	8
	Totals	6	17	22	5	Grand Total 50

If there were no correlation between success in English and Science, i.e., if the two variables were independent, then the 8 pupils who obtained A in English ought to be distributed

among the four Science categories in the proportion of
6:17:22:5. The 16 pupils who obtained B in English should
be distributed among A, B, C and D in Science in the same
proportion, and so on. Similarly, the 6 pupils who obtained
A in Science should be distributed on the null hypothesis in
the proportion of 8:16:18:8 in the four English categories.

The contingency table above is a table of obtained frequencies, or—as we say—of O-values. We may now construct
a corresponding table of expected frequencies, or of E-values.
Thus, the E-value for A in English and A in Science is given
by $8 \times \frac{6}{50}$; the E-value for A in English and B in Science is
$8 \times \frac{17}{50}$; the E-value for A in English and C in Science is
$8 \times \frac{22}{50}$; the E-value for A in English and D in Science is
$8 \times \frac{5}{50}$. The total number of expected A marks in English is,
of course, $8 \times \frac{6}{50} + 8 \times \frac{17}{50} + 8 \times \frac{22}{50} + 8 \times \frac{5}{50} = 8$. In
this manner E-values for each cell may be found, and a table,
such as Table XXVIII, may be constructed.

TABLE XXVIII

THEORETICALLY EXPECTED DISTRIBUTION
OF EXAMINATION RESULTS

	A	B	C	D
A	0·96	2·72	3·52	0·80
B	1·92	5·44	7·04	1·60
C	2·16	6·12	7·92	1·80
D	0·96	2·72	3·52	0·80

To compute χ^2 we must first obtain $(O - E)$ values cell by
cell, then $(O - E)^2$ values, then $\left[\dfrac{(O - E)^2}{E} \right]$ values, and
finally, to obtain $\Sigma \left[\dfrac{(O - E)^2}{E} \right]$, we must add up all the
$\left[\dfrac{(O - E)^2}{E} \right]$ values.

The $(O - E)$ values are given in Table XXIX.

TABLE XXIX
·(O − E) VALUES

	A	B	C	D
A	1·04	0·28	−0·52	−0·80
B	0·08	1·56	−0·04	−1·60
C	−0·16	−1·12	0·08	1·20
D	−0·96	−0·72	0·48	1·20

Squaring the values cell by cell we arrive at Table XXX.

TABLE XXX
$(O − E)^2$ VALUES

	A	B	C	D
A	1·08	0·08	0·27	0·64
B	0·01	2·44	0·00	2·56
C	0·03	1·26	0·01	1·44
D	0·92	0·52	0·23	1·44

Dividing the values by the E appropriate for each cell, we tabulate the results as shown in Table XXXI.

TABLE XXXI
$$\frac{(O − E)^2}{E} \text{ VALUES}$$

	A	B	C	D	Totals
A	1·12	0·03	0·08	0·80	2·03
B	0·01	0·45	0·00	1·60	2·06
C	0·01	0·21	0·00	0·80	1·02
D	0·96	0·19	0·07	1·80	3·02
Totals	2·10	0·88	0·15	5·00	8·13

Thus, $\chi^2 = 8·13$.

Having arrived thus far, we must now look up appropriate tables to see if the divergence between the obtained results and those expected from the null hypothesis is significant, say, at the 5 per cent and the 1 per cent levels.

We may use Table XXXII; though a greatly abbreviated version of Fisher's original tables, the table is good enough for our present purpose. Before using it, however, we must consider the question of the number of degrees of freedom.

The number of degrees of freedom in a contingency table where each cell gives a frequency value is the number of cells to which arbitrary values may be assigned, the sums obtained from each row and column remaining fixed. If r is the number of rows and c is the number of columns in a table, then the number of degrees of freedom is given by

$$df = (r - 1)(c - 1)$$

In the case of our example $r = 4$ and $c = 4$. Therefore, $df = (4 - 1)(4 - 1) = 9$.

We see that when $df = 9$ the value of χ^2 must be much greater than $8 \cdot 13$ for the divergence between the expected and obtained results to be significant even at the 5 per cent level. Thus, we cannot conclude with any confidence from our data that there is a contingency or association between successes in English and Science, and the null hypothesis of the independence of the variables must be retained. This does not, of course, mean that the two variables are independent. If we suspect that they are not, we must consider many more than 50 pairs of papers; this might enable us to assert with greater confidence that the divergence, such as it may be, of expected from obtained results is statistically significant.

The Expectation of a Uniform Distribution. In the last example the expected frequencies for the different cells were in proportions such as would have resulted if the two variables had been completely independent of one another. Sometimes, however, the expected frequencies may be distributed uniformly. This could be regarded as a special simple case of the type of problem discussed in the previous section.

Consider, for example, a report regarding the number of road accidents in a certain district on each day of a particular week, as set out in Table XXXIII.

TABLE XXXII

CHI-SQUARED VALUES CORRESPONDING TO $P = 0·05$ AND $P = 0·01$

Degrees of Freedom	1	2	3	4	5	6	7	8	9	10	11	12
$P = 0·05$	3·84	5·99	7·82	9·49	11·07	12·59	14·07	15·51	16·92	18·31	19·68	21·03
$P = 0·01$	6·64	9·21	11·35	13·28	15·09	16·81	18·48	20·09	21·67	23·21	24·73	26·22
Degrees of Freedom	13	14	15	16	17	18	19	20	21	22	23	24
$P = 0·05$	22·36	23·69	25·00	26·30	27·59	28·87	30·14	31·41	32·67	33·92	35·17	36·42
$P = 0·01$	27·69	29·14	30·58	32·00	33·41	34·81	36·19	37·57	38·93	40·29	41·64	42·98

Abridged from Table IV of Fisher: Statistical Methods for Research Workers, published by Oliver and Boyd Ltd., Edinburgh, by permission of the author and publishers.

TABLE XXXIII

INCIDENCE OF ROAD ACCIDENTS DAY-BY-DAY

Sun.	Mon.	Tues.	Wed.	Th.	Fri.	Sat.	Total
17	16	10	13	15	11	16	98

Does the meagre information justify an assumption that the accidents are not uniformly distributed over the week? On the null hypothesis of a uniform distribution of accidents, we must expect the following (set out in Table XXXIV).

TABLE XXXIV

EXPECTATION OF ROAD ACCIDENTS DAY-BY-DAY

Sun.	Mon.	Tues.	Wed.	Th.	Fri.	Sat.	Total
14	14	14	14	14	14	14	98

We may now work out the value of χ^2 in order to find out whether the divergence between the obtained and expected distributions is significant. This may conveniently be done in a tabular form (as shown in Table XXXV).

TABLE XXXV

$(O - E)$ AND $(O - E)^2$ VALUES

	Sun.	Mon.	Tues.	Wed.	Th.	Fri.	Sat.
$(O - E)$	3	2	−4	−1	1	−3	2
$(O - E)^2$	9	4	16	1	1	9	4

Since the value of E is the same for each cell, we may first add up $(O - E)^2$ values and then divide the same by $E = 14$. Thus,

$$\Sigma(O - E)^2 = 44$$

In this case:

$$\Sigma[(O - E)^2/E] = \Sigma(O - E)^2/E$$
$$= 44/14$$
$$\therefore \chi^2 = 3\cdot14$$

Now the number of degrees of freedom, $(r - 1)(c - 1) = 6$. This may be seen directly from the definition of df. We see that if n is the number of comparisons made (i.e., the number of cases), then $df = n - 1$; here, of course, $df = 7 - 1 = 6$.

Looking up Table XXXII we note that the value of χ^2 should have been at least $12\cdot59$ for the divergence between the expected and obtained distributions to be significant. It is, therefore, clear that any conclusion as to the lack of uniformity of accident distribution over the seven days of the week would be a rash one. We must retain the null hypothesis, suspending judgment until further data are obtained.

Chi-Squared Test and the Agreement between Obtained and Normal Distributions. Quite often we have to deal with a large number of measures of a variable and we may wish to know whether we should be justified in regarding their distribution as normal. The obtained distribution curve can be plotted; so can the theoretical normal curve. Our problem, then, is that of goodness of fit of the observed and the theoretical distribution curves. Again the problem may be tackled by means of the chi-squared test.

Suppose that we are dealing with a distribution of 1,000 cases ($N = 1,000$), its standard deviation being 5 units of the variable ($\sigma = 5$). The frequency curve of this distribution is shown, marked "obtained curve", in Fig. 21, where σ is represented by 4 units on the scale.

The first problem facing us is to determine the normal curve based on $N = 1,000$ and $\sigma = 5$. The central ordinate is given by

$$y_0 = N/\sigma\sqrt{2\pi} \text{ (see Table XXIV)}$$
$$= 1000/5\sqrt{2\pi} = 79\cdot8$$

We can now plot the normal curve which is expected on our null hypothesis. A test of the hypothesis will consist of establishing the significance of the divergence (or of the goodness of fit) between the observed and expected curves.

Now we must decide at how many points we are going to

measure the difference between observed and expected ordinates, $(O - E)$. It is accurate enough to do it every $\frac{1}{2}\sigma$ as far as $+3\sigma$ and -3σ away from the mean. We can conveniently tabulate our results as shown in Table XXXVI; the tabulated values are only approximate.

Having evaluated the chi-squared, we now have to look up the tables to see if the divergence between the observed and expected curves which the χ^2 represents is significant at the 5 per cent and 1 per cent levels.

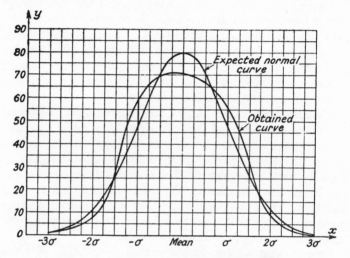

FIG. 21. OBSERVED AND EXPECTED CURVES

However, before we can use the tables we must again consider the question of the number of degrees of freedom. We have computed the differences between the O-values and the E-values at 13 points. It might, therefore, be thought that the number of degrees of freedom is 12. It may be shown, however, that the appropriate value when a comparison is made between an expected normal curve and an observed one is $(n - 3)$. Thus in this case we may take the value of d.f. = 10.

The sum of the entries in Column 4 of Table XXXVI is 8·66. Now, using Table XXXII, we see that for 10 degrees of freedom, even at the 5 per cent level of confidence, the value of χ^2 is over 18. We must, therefore, conclude that different as the obtained curve in Fig. 21 may seem, it is not significantly different from a normal curve based on the σ-value of the obtained distribution. Therefore we are obliged to retain the null hypothesis that the 1,000 individual cases of our example are normally scattered. In other words, it cannot be concluded that a normal curve does not fit the obtained distribution.

TABLE XXXVI

EVALUATION OF χ^2; $N = 1{,}000$, $\sigma = 5$

Col. 1 σ-value	Col. 2 $(O - E)$	Col. 3 $(O - E)^2$	Col. 4 $\dfrac{(O - E)^2}{E}$
-3σ	0·0	0·0	0·0
$-2\frac{1}{2}\sigma$	$-1·0$	1·0	0·25
-2σ	$-3·0$	9·0	0·80
$-1\frac{1}{2}\sigma$	$+2·0$	4·0	0·15
$-\sigma$	$+12·0$	144·0	3·00
$-\frac{1}{2}\sigma$	0·0	0·0	0·0
0	$-10·0$	100·0	1·25
$\frac{1}{2}\sigma$	$-3·0$	9·0	0·13
σ	$+8·0$	64·0	1·33
$1\frac{1}{2}\sigma$	$+6·0$	36·0	1·40
2σ	$-1·0$	1·0	0·10
$2\frac{1}{2}\sigma$	$-1·0$	1·0	0·25
3σ	0·0	0·0	0·0

$$\chi^2 = \Sigma[(O - E)^2/E] = 8·66$$

CHAPTER IX

The Principles of Correlation

Statistics of Relationship. In the early chapters we were concerned with the computation of "descriptive" statistics. We sought simple numerical descriptions of distributions, such as central tendency or variability. Later we went beyond the mere description of the distribution within the sample. By considering the general theory of the reliability or significance of statistics, we learnt something of the conditions under which it is permissible to generalise from the sample to the parent population. Thus, we have been concerned so far mainly with statistics that describe quantitatively certain characteristics or attributes of either a sample or a total population.

The aim of many investigations, however, in various fields goes beyond the description of the distributions of separate characteristics. The research worker must also study the conditions under which different degrees of incidence of separate characteristics occur. These conditions themselves are, in effect, a group of different characteristics. Therefore, often the general problem of the scientist becomes the discovery, the analysis, and the verification of the relationships between two or more characteristics.

A coefficient of correlation is a single number that tells us to what extent two characteristics are related. It tells us to what extent variations in the incidence of one characteristic of a population go with variations in another characteristic of the same population. With the help of such knowledge, the scientist can make predictions; and further, he may be able to control one thing by manipulating another.

Thus, if we knew that the higher an army recruit's score in a mechanical aptitude test, the higher the average degree of proficiency he is likely to exhibit after training, then in future we could use scores in this test to predict the level of proficiency. There would be a high degree of correlation between scores in the aptitude test and mechanical proficiency. The existence of the relationship between these two things would be discovered by finding a coefficient of correlation between the scores of a number of recruits, and measures of the success of their mechanical performance later on. We could, however, do more than predict the future success of a group of recruits. We could in effect control the level of efficiency by selecting for this particular field only those recruits who scored high in the test.

For just such reasons is the economist interested in relationships that may be discovered in economic and business time series. Such relationships enable him to predict costs, sales and prices, on the basis of some other series with which these may be related. The sociologist may be interested in the relationship between age and fertility; the education officer, in intelligence and scholastic achievement. The personnel executive may be concerned with the relationship between age and production; and the psychologist, between patterns of interest and occupational success. In general, all research work leading to prediction and control in the field of human affairs is made possible because statistical techniques exist, enabling the research worker to examine the existence, degree, and direction of any relationship there may be between two or more characteristics for which measuring devices have been developed.

The coefficient of correlation is, then, a statistical device which can be very valuable if it is properly applied. However, perhaps nowhere in the whole field of statistical procedure are errors more frequent than in the use and the interpretation of correlation techniques. In this chapter we shall be concerned first of all with the methods of calculating the coefficients; then, we shall note the more common sources of error so that the reader may be continually on his guard if and when he uses the methods.

Some Examples of Correlation. The coefficient of correlation is a simple arithmetic figure which will indicate the extent to which two variables are correlated. It is a pure number that has no connection with the units in which our variables are measured. It varies from a value of $+1\cdot00$, which means perfect positive relationship, down through the value zero which indicates no relationship at all, until it reaches its lower limit −1·00, indicating perfect negative correlation.

For the purpose of illustrating different degrees of relationship, let us assume that we have measured for each individual in a sample two quantitative characteristics X and Y. Fig. 22 indicates the sort of relationships that might result.

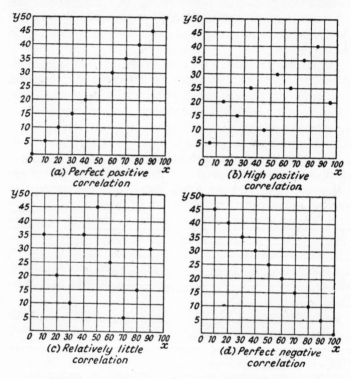

FIG. 22. CORRELATION BETWEEN TWO VARIABLES

In each case in Fig. 22 measures of the X characteristic are marked along the horizontal axis, and measures of the Y characteristic along the vertical one. Case (a) illustrates perfect positive correlation. There is obviously a relationship between the two sets of measures. High values of X go with high values of Y, and conversely low values of X are found with low values of Y. Moreover, the agreement is an exact one; any measure of X is always exactly twice its corresponding Y-value. There is direct proportion between the two series of measures, and the coefficient of correlation is 1·00. The example is a fictitious one. Rarely, if ever, is such exact agreement between two things experienced in the social sciences. The example, however, illustrates one limit of relationship.

Case (b) also illustrates a positive correlation, but this time the correlation is not perfect. Again it is obvious that high values of X "tend" to go with high values of Y. The tendency is a pronounced one, although the relationship is not perfect; so we should expect a high positive correlation coefficient, but something less than 1·00. The coefficient of correlation calculated for this case is 0·67. In case (a) all the individuals line up in a perfect file from the lowest to the highest. In case (b), they tend to fan out or diverge from a strict line. It is, in effect, this divergence from a straight line that illustrates the difference between a perfect and a high positive correlation.

A glance at case (c) in Fig. 22 indicates that the spreading effect here is much greater. There is no obvious relationship between measures of X and their corresponding Y-values. As the values of X increase, there is nothing to indicate what happens to the values of Y. An individual with a high X-value is likely to be almost anywhere with regard to his Y-value. Not only do the spots on the diagram not fall on a line, but there is also no apparent line from which they appear to diverge. The scatter is haphazard. We should expect a correlation coefficient of zero, or something negligibly small. The calculated coefficient in this case is in fact −0·18.

The situation that occurs when there is a negative correlation is illustrated in case (d). Here again the relationship is a perfect one, but this time it is of an inverse order. As the values of the X-measures increase, those of the Y-measures decrease. As the relationship is a perfect one, the "size" of the correlation coefficient is 1·00. As the "direction" of relationship is "inverse" and not "direct", the sign of the coefficient is minus and not plus. This illustrates the other limit of relationship, but here again it must be pointed out that such perfect relationships between things do not exist in the social sciences.

The correlation coefficient is, then, a mere number like an average, or a standard deviation; and like them it supplies important information. Let us now turn to the methods used in calculating these coefficients.

The Product-Moment Coefficient of Correlation. As our first example let us consider some data on production in the punch-press shop of a factory. Suppose a number of operators have each, in a given time, punched a number of pieces correctly and also spoiled or wasted a certain number. The management is reviewing its policy with regard to the speed of the work recommended and with regard to incentives in the form of bonuses. It is important to know whether any relationship exists (and if so how much) between quantity produced and quantity spoiled.

In a department of the shop in which ten operators work, the production and wastage figures are as indicated in Table XXXVII. To examine the relationship between production

TABLE XXXVII

PRODUCTION AND SPOILAGE RATES PER HOUR
FOR TEN PRESS OPERATORS

Operator	Units Produced	Units Spoiled
1	94	4
2	98	5
3	106	6
4	114	7
5	107	6
6	93	5
7	98	6
8	88	4
9	103	7
10	95	5

and wastage we will use the standard kind of coefficient of correlation, the one most commonly computed. This is known as the Pearson-Bravais product-moment coefficient. The basic formula is

$$r_{xy} = \frac{\Sigma xy}{N \sigma_x \sigma_y}$$

where r_{xy} — correlation between the two variables X and Y.

  x — the deviation of any X value from the mean of all the X values.

  y — the deviation of any Y value from the mean of all the Y values.

  σ_x — the standard deviation of the X values.

  σ_y — the standard deviation of the Y values.

  N — the total number of cases.

All the above terms should be familiar to the reader. The deviations referred to were used in an earlier chapter when the method of computing the standard deviation was outlined. The steps necessary for the calculation of the correlation coefficient are set out in Table XXXVIII.

The steps are as follows:

1. List in parallel columns the paired values of the two variables X and Y. In this example X is an operator's production figure, and Y his spoilage figure. It is important to make sure that corresponding values are together.

2. Sum these two columns and determine M_x, the mean of the X values, and M_y the mean of the Y values. In Table XXXVIII these are: 99·6 the mean production figure, and 5·5 the mean spoilage figure.

3. Determine for each X value its deviation from M_x and list them in Column 3. Be careful to include the algebraic sign. To determine x, simply subtract M_x from each X value.

4. In a similar manner determine for each Y value its deviation from M_y, and list them in Column 4.

5. Check the determination of the deviations by summing Columns 3 and 4. In each case the sum should be zero.

6. Square each x deviation and list the squares in Column 5. Note that all signs are now plus.

7. Square the y deviations and list them in Column 6.

8. Sum Columns 5 and 6 to get Σx^2 and Σy^2. In the table these are 450·40 and 10·50.

9. Calculate σ_x from the formula

$$\sigma_x = \sqrt{(\Sigma x^2/N)}$$

Note that in this formula there is no correction factor to be considered as we are using deviations from the true mean. In the calculations below the table, σ_x comes to 6·711.

10. Similarly calculate σ_y. In this example it comes to 1·025.

TABLE XXXVIII

CORRELATION BETWEEN PRODUCTION AND WASTAGE
FOR TEN PUNCH-PRESS OPERATORS

	Col. 1 X	Col. 2 Y	Col. 3 x	Col. 4 y	Col. 5 x^2	Col. 6 y^2	Col. 7 xy
	94	4	−5·6	−1·5	31·36	2·25	+8·4
	98	5	−1·6	−0·5	2·56	0·25	+0·8
	106	6	+6·4	+0·5	40·96	0·25	+3·2
	114	7	+14·4	+1·5	207·36	2·25	+21·6
	107	6	+7·4	+0·5	54·76	0·25	+3·7
	93	5	−6·6	−0·5	43·56	0·25	+3·3
	98	6	−1·6	+0·5	2·56	0·25	−0·8
	88	4	−11·6	−1·5	34·56	2·25	+17·4
	103	7	+3·4	+1·5	11·56	2·25	+5·1
	95	5	−4·6	−0·5	21·16	0·25	+2·3
Sums	996	55	0·0	0·0	450·40	10·50	65·0
Means	99·6	5·5					

$$\sigma_x = \sqrt{(\Sigma x^2/N)} = \sqrt{(550\cdot4/10)} = \sqrt{55\cdot04} = 6\cdot711$$
$$\sigma_y = \sqrt{(\Sigma y^2/N)} = \sqrt{(10\cdot50/10)} = \sqrt{1\cdot05} = 1\cdot025$$
$$r_{xy} = \Sigma xy/N \cdot \sigma_x \cdot \sigma_y = 65\cdot0/10 \times 6\cdot711 \times 1\cdot025$$
$$= 65\cdot0/68\cdot8$$
$$= +0\cdot94$$

11. Multiply each value in Column 3 by the corresponding value in Column 4 to get the *xy* products. List these in Column 7. Be careful to get the algebraic signs correct.

12. Sum Column 7 algebraically to get Σxy. Table XXXVIII shows this to be 65·0. We now have all the information necessary to calculate the coefficient of correlation from our formula. The calculations follow the table and result in a coefficient of +0·94.

This is a very high value and indicates a distinct relationship between speed of production and amount spoiled. Later in this chapter we shall consider the significance and reliability of correlation coefficients.

There is a shorter and simpler method of calculating this coefficient. It is shorter in that σ_x and σ_y are not calculated, and may be used when the standard deviations are not required for further statistical computation. The formula for this calculation is

$$r_{xy} = \Sigma xy / \sqrt{(\Sigma x^2)(\Sigma y^2)}$$

All the information required is given in Table XXXVIII, and the calculation is as follows:

$$r_{xy} = 65 \cdot 0 / \sqrt{(450 \cdot 4 \times 10 \cdot 5)} = 65 \cdot 0 / 68 \cdot 8 = + 0 \cdot 94$$

The solution, it will be noted, leads to exactly the same coefficient.

How many places of decimals should be used in stating the coefficient? In the present example we have used two. It must be stressed, however, that the size of the sample is very small, and the corresponding sampling error is liable to be relatively large. Anything more than two places of decimals would be unjustifiable in these circumstances. When larger samples are used, say with $N = 200$ or more, then it is usual to calculate r to three places of decimals. Small numbers are used in the examples in this book simply to make it easy for the reader to follow the computations. Despite the existence of special statistical techniques for treating small samples, the reader is strongly advised to take as large a sample as is practically available (so long as it is reasonably amenable to statistical computation) when starting out on an investigation.

The Scatter Diagram. When the sample is large or even when it is moderate in size and no calculating machine is available, the methods of computation described above become very tedious. The usual procedure in such circumstances is to use grouped data.

The general principles we followed when grouping data for frequency distributions apply here. We are in fact grouping two lots of data into class intervals and presenting them in the form of frequency distributions. A special method is used, however, in which the two groupings are done at the same time and presented in what is called a "scatter diagram". An example will illustrate the method.

Suppose for the purpose of our example that a factory has inaugurated a training scheme whereby recruits are trained in the techniques and skills of their jobs before being posted to the various shops. In assessing the value of the training programme, the management wishes to know whether there is any relation between the scores obtained by the recruits during their training course and their subsequent success on the job. In order to determine this, some quantitative estimate of job success is required. This is achieved by having the supervisors rate the individuals concerned on a rating scale for production, efficiency, and job knowledge. The rating scale, used after say one year, is so designed that it will yield a total score for each individual, and this score can be taken as a quantitative estimate of job success. Each individual concerned has now two scores, and we are in a position to tackle the problem.

The scatter diagram or "scattergram", as it is often called, depicting the paired scores for 140 operatives is shown in Fig. 23. The construction of this chart is quite simple. Along the top are listed the class intervals of the training scores with their limits; and down the left-hand side the class intervals and limits for the distribution of job success scores are set out. Each of the 140 operatives is represented in the body of the table for both training score and success score. He is represented by a tally mark which depicts his two scores.

To illustrate the tallying process, suppose one worker scored 68 on the training course, and achieved a rating of 21 on job success. A tally is placed for him in the cell of the diagram where the column for interval 65–69 in training score intersects the row for interval 20–24 in job success score.

TRAINING SCORES

JOB SUCCESS RATINGS	50-54	55-59	60-64	65-69	70-74	75-79	80-84	85-89	90-94	95-99	f_y
45-49								1	1		2
40-44					1	2	2	3	3		11
35-39				1	2	4	2	5	3	1	18
30-34				3	4	3	5	1	2		18
25-29			2	4	7	5	5		1	1	25
20-24		1	1	7	9	6	3				27
15-19	1	4	5	4	2	3	1				20
10-14		2	4	1	1	1		1			10
5-9	1	3	1								5
0-4	1	2	1								4
f_x	3	12	14	20	26	24	18	11	10	2	140 N

FIG. 23. SCATTER DIAGRAM

When all the tallying is completed the cell frequency, or the number of cases in each cell, is entered on the diagram. Next the cell frequencies in each row are summed and the totals are entered for each row in the last column headed f_y. This column now gives the frequency distribution for the job success scores. The cell frequencies in each column are now summed, and the totals are entered in the last row which has the title f_x. This row depicts the frequency distribution for the training programme scores.

Both the f_x column and the f_y row must total 140, the number of men in all. The fact that these totals both equal N is not, however, a check on the tallying process. It is quite easy to put a tally mark in the wrong cell, and the only way to check the tallying is to do it twice, or better still, have two people do it and compare the results.

Calculating r from the Scatter Diagram. The preparation of the scatter diagram is the first step necessary for the calculation of a Pearson r when the data are grouped. For the calculation itself the formula is suitably altered, becoming

$$r_{xy} = \frac{\dfrac{\Sigma x'y'}{N} - (c'_x c'_y)}{(\sigma_x')(\sigma_y')}$$

where x' — the deviation from the guessed mean of the X-series in terms of the class interval unit.

y' — the deviation from the guessed mean of the Y-series in terms of the class interval unit.

c'_x — the correction factor in X for having used a guessed, and not a true mean of X; it is also calculated in class interval units.

c'_y — a similar correction factor in Y, also in class interval units.

σ_x' — the standard deviation of X in class interval units.

σ_y' — the standard deviation of Y in class interval units.

This at first sight, no doubt, looks a most complicated process. It must be stressed, however, that we are not using a new formula. It is exactly the same as that used in the early part of this chapter when computing r from ungrouped data. In this case, however, all calculations are in terms of the class interval as the unit and in terms of a guessed mean, so that the formula has to be adjusted to take account of these factors. The sole purpose of using a guessed mean and a class interval unit is to make the computation simpler. Complicated as it may appear, the working is really quite straightforward, and the reader has to concentrate chiefly on the manner of setting the work out and the order in which the steps are taken.

Table XXXIX will serve as an illustration of the computation required. It is called a correlation table, and contains the paired job success and training scores from the scatter diagram in the form of frequencies for the two sets of class intervals. To the right of this frequency table six columns are ruled, and below, six rows are ruled. These will eventually contain data concerning the job success and training score distributions respectively.

With the table prepared as explained, the procedure is as follows:

1. Sum all the rows to get the total frequencies for each class interval of the job success scores, and enter them in Column 1 under the heading f_y. For example, for the class interval 40–44 the row contains numbers 1, 2, 2, 3, and 3, and these are summed giving a total frequency of 11 that appears as the second item in the column.

2. Similarly sum all the columns and enter the totals in Row 1 to get the frequency distribution of the training scores. This row is titled f_x. Thus the training score interval 65–69 contains numbers 1, 3, 4, 7, 4, and 1, and when these are summed they give 20 which appears as the fourth item in Row f_x.

3. Sum Column f_y and Row f_x, and check that they each have a total equal to N. In this example N is 140.

4. Look down the Column f_y and guess the interval that contains the mean. It does not matter whether you make a good guess or not, but the better the guess the simpler the calculation. It is usual to pick the largest frequency. A glance at the table shows that 27 is the largest frequency. This is the frequency for the job success score interval 20–24. Double lines are ruled above and below the row containing this frequency.

5. Similarly look along the Row f_x containing the distribution of the training scores, and again guess the interval that contains the mean. The largest frequency is 26 for the interval 70–74. Double lines are ruled on either side of the column containing the frequency 26.

6. In Column 2 headed y' are entered the deviations of the

success score intervals from the interval containing the guessed mean. These deviations are in units of class intervals. Thus the row above the one bounded by double lines has a deviation of 1, the next above 2, and so on. Similarly the row below the one bounded by double lines has a deviation of -1, the next -2, and so on.

7. Row 2 titled x' is filled in, giving the deviations of the training score intervals from the one containing the guessed mean. Again it will be noted these deviations are in terms of class intervals.

8. Fill in Column 3 by multiplying the corresponding entries of Columns 1 and 2 to get fy'. Sum this column algebraically to get $\Sigma fy'$. In the table $\Sigma fy' = 98$. Be careful with the signs.

9. Similarly complete Row 3 by multiplying the items from Rows 1 and 2 to get fx', and sum the row to get $\Sigma fx'$. In the table $\Sigma fx' = 47$.

10. Multiply Column 3 by Column 2, item by item, to get fy'^2, and enter the results in Column 4. All the signs, it will be noted, are now plus. Sum this column to get $\Sigma fy'^2$. In the table $\Sigma fy'^2 = 654$.

11. Similarly complete Row 4, and sum the row to get $\Sigma fx'^2$. In our example $\Sigma fx'^2 = 637$.

12. To get the $x'y'$ products the procedure is as follows. Take in turn each cell that contains a frequency, and multiply the y' value for its row, by the x' value for its column, and enter the product (in brackets) in the upper left-hand corner of the cell. Be careful with the sign.

13. Multiply the $x'y'$ product of each cell by the frequency in the cell to get the total $x'y'$ product. Enter this total without brackets in the bottom right-hand corner of each cell. The cells bounded by double lines have, of course, no $x'y'$ products as their deviations are 0. It will be noted that all the total $x'y'$ products in the top right-hand quarter and bottom left-hand quarter of the tables are $+$, while those in the top left-hand and bottom right-hand quarters are $-$. This must always be so.

14. Sum all the $+x'y'$ products for each row, and enter the totals in Column 5. Sum all the $-x'y'$ products for each row and enter the totals in Column 6. To get the grand total $\Sigma x'y'$, sum Columns 5 and 6, and subtract the total of Column

6 from the total of Column 5. In our table $\Sigma x'y' = 488 - 30 = 458.$

15. Sum the $+x'y'$ products for each column, and also the $-x'y'$ products, and enter them in Rows 5 and 6. Sum Rows 5 and 6 and get the grand total $\Sigma x'y'$. This is a check on step 14. The sums of Rows 5 and 6 must equal the sums of Columns 5 and 6 respectively.

All the information is now available to calculate r. The steps in the calculation are shown below, and are self-explanatory. The result shows that there is a correlation of 0·70 between training course scores and subsequent merit rating scores.

$$c'x = \frac{\Sigma fx'}{N} = \frac{47}{140} = 0.336$$

$$c'y = \frac{\Sigma fy'}{N} = \frac{98}{140} = 0.700$$

$$\sigma_x' = \sqrt{\frac{\Sigma fx'^2}{N} - (c'x)^2} = \sqrt{\frac{637}{140} - 0.113} = 2.11$$

$$\sigma_y' = \sqrt{\frac{\Sigma fy'^2}{N} - (c'y)^2} = \sqrt{\frac{654}{140} - 0.49} = 2.05$$

$$r_{xy} = \frac{\dfrac{\Sigma x'y'}{N} - (c'x.c'y)}{(\sigma_x')(\sigma_y')}$$

$$\frac{\dfrac{458}{140} - 0.336 \times 0.700}{2.11 \times 2.05}$$

$$= \frac{3.28 - 0.235}{4.32} = \frac{3.045}{4.32}$$

$$= 0.70$$

The Size of the Correlation Coefficient. What degree of relationship does a correlation of 0·70 indicate? Any coefficient that is not zero and that is significant statistically indicates some degree of relationship. It is important to understand, however, that the degree of relationship is not proportional to the size of the coefficient. A coefficient of 0·60 does not mean that the relationship is exactly twice as strong as one indicated by a coefficient of 0·30.

The correlation coefficient is an index number, not a measurement like inches, shillings, or tons. The correct interpretation depends always on the particular problem being investigated and the purpose for which the coefficient is being calculated. What would be considered a high correlation in one investigation may be considered a low one in another. However, speaking generally, the following is a rough but useful guide to the degree of relationship indicated by the size of the coefficients.

0·90–1·00   Very high correlation; very strong relationship.

0·70–0·90   High correlation: marked relationship.

0·40–0·70   Moderate correlation; substantial relationship.

0·20–0·40   Low correlation: a definite relationship but a small one.

less than 0·20   A slight correlation: relationship so small as to be negligible.

This interpretation of course is only valid for correlation coefficients that satisfy the tests of reliability.

Reliability of Correlation Coefficients. The mere statement of the value of a correlation coefficient is not in itself sufficient evidence of relationship between two variables. Like all statistics computed from samples taken at random, correlation coefficients are subject to sampling errors. In the previous example the data on one hundred and forty cases yielded a coefficient of 0·70 leading us to believe that in the circumstances described there was a considerable relationship between training scores and success on the job. If, however, we took a second and third and fourth sample should we continue to get a value in the neighbourhood of 0·70? Or, would the successive values fluctuate considerably? In general, how reliable is the calculated coefficient?

In earlier chapters the significance and reliability of the means of samples were tested by comparing them with their standard errors. The reader will remember that if means were to be calculated from a number of samples, provided the samples were large, these means would themselves tend to be distributed normally. The standard error of the mean is simply the standard deviation of all these sample means. Knowledge of this standard error enabled us to state the degree of confidence we could have that the true mean lay within certain specified limits.

The same method may in certain cases be used in interpreting correlation coefficients. The standard error of r is given by the formula

$$\sigma_r = (1 - r^2)/\sqrt{(N - 1)}$$

When $N = 140$ and $r = 0.70$, as in the example above,

$$\sigma_r = [1 - (0.70)^2]/\sqrt{(140 - 1)} = 0.51/11.8 = 0.043$$

It is sufficient to state most standard errors to two significant figures. This result enables us to estimate with varying degrees of confidence how close our computed r is to the true population r. The odds are about 2 to 1 that our value of 0.70 does not deviate from the population r by more than 0.043. The odds are 20 to 1 that it does not deviate more than twice its standard error, or 0.086, and 100 to 1 that it does not deviate by as much as 0.111, or 2.58 times the standard error. In normal statistical practice the odds of 100 to 1 are considered very satisfactory; thus with a correlation coefficient of 0.70, and a standard error of 0.043, there is less than one chance in a hundred that the true population coefficient falls outside the limits of 0.70 ± 0.111, or 0.81 and 0.59. The coefficient that we arrived at is, then, a reliable indication of quite a high correlation, and we can feel assured that further sampling would not yield a low correlation coefficient.

It should be pointed out here that sampling distributions of correlation coefficients, unlike those of most other statistics, are not symmetrical ones. The shape of the particular sampling distribution, in fact, depends on both the size of the population correlation coefficient, and the size of the sample. The former affects the sampling distribution symmetry. Correlation coefficients have a very restricted range, from $+1$ to -1. No coefficient can exceed these limits, so that when the population r-value approaches them, the sampling distribution becomes more and more skewed. Only when the population r-value is in the neighbourhood of zero, can the sampling distribution be expected to be a symmetrical one.

Does this mean then that the calculation of a standard error, which assumes a symmetrical distribution, is no guide to reliability? In theory it is applicable only to small r-values and large N-values. In practice, however, one need not worry about the effect of skewness for correlation coefficients that range from, say, $+0.80$ to -0.80, provided the sample is a large one. The larger the sample the smaller the dispersion of r-values, so the moral is take large samples and avoid troublesome problems of reliability.

The Significance of Small r-Values. When a calculated correlation coefficient is numerically small, but either negative or positive, the question of reliability becomes more important. We are not now only concerned with the "amount" of relationship, but the question arises "is there any relationship at all?" The possibility is that the population r-value is zero, and our calculated r, the size of the sample being what it is, has just occurred merely by random sampling.

The best approach to solving this problem is to assume that the population r-value is zero, and then ask ourselves the question "could the calculated coefficient have arisen by random sampling?" This is another application of the null hypothesis. When the population correlation coefficient is zero, then the standard error is given by the formula

$$\sigma_{r_0} = 1/\sqrt{(N-1)}$$

and by the use of this formula we can answer our question with varying degrees of confidence.

Let us assume, for example, that a given problem yielded a calculated r of 0.16 from a sample of 401 cases. Applying the formula,

$$\sigma_{r_0} = 1/\sqrt{400}$$
$$= 1/20$$
$$= 0.05$$

Our hypothesis now is that the population r is zero, and the value of 0.05 arose merely due to errors caused by random sampling. The test of this hypothesis lies in the examination of the critical ratio, t, where

$$t = r/\sigma_{r_0}$$

In our example

$$t = 0.16/0.05 = 3.20$$

This means, in effect, that the calculated coefficient is more than three times as large as its standard error, and rarely could such a correction occur by random sampling in a population where r is in fact zero. Thus we can reject the null hypothesis and declare that there is a significant relationship.

With what degree of confidence can we make such a declaration? The larger the t, the less likely could r occur by random sampling. At the 5 per cent level of confidence, a t of 1·96 indicates a "significant correlation". This means that we can reject the null hypothesis and be wrong only five times in a hundred. We can be more confident in our rejection of the null hypothesis if we set as our criterion a t-value as large as 2·58. This corresponds to the 1 per cent level of confidence, and means that there is less than one chance in a hundred that a t as large or larger could have occurred due to chance.

In general a t greater than 1·96 but less than 2·58 may be taken as indicating a "significant" correlation while a t of 2·58 or greater may be taken as indicating a "very significant" correlation. Anything below 1·96, however, should ordinarily be treated as "insignificant". This does not mean that in fact there is no correlation; it simply means that the existence of a relationship is "not proven".

The reader is warned against accepting correlation coefficients at face value. It is most important to examine the reliability of the figure, and particular notice must be taken of small coefficients, as a small positive r might arise in a sample when in fact the population r-value is small but negative.

Finally, even a high correlation between A and B does not signify a cause-and-effect relationship. It signifies only association. A may in fact be the cause of B; B may be the cause of A; or A and B may vary concomitantly due to a third, but unknown, factor C. Statistics alone will give no answer. When functional relations are examined by the use of statistical techniques, the analysis must always be considered incomplete until a logical connection has been traced between the variables.

Significance of difference between means when measures are correlated. In considering the question of the statistical significance of a difference between two means in earlier chapters we noted that the formula we used for the standard error of the difference between means was valid only when the two sets of data were uncorrelated. In practice such two sets of measures are by no means always uncorrelated. Correlated samples are encountered when two sets of measurements are obtained from the same group of subjects, or from two groups where subjects are matched pair by pair. A typical example of correlated measures occurs when, say, an achievement test is given to a single group of children before and after a course of coaching. Those individuals who were good on first testing will very likely be good on second testing also, and those who were poor to start with will probably remain poor.

The coefficient of correlation must be taken into account in the computation of the standard error of the difference between two means. The formula is

$$\sigma_D = \sqrt{\sigma_{M_1}^2 + \sigma_{M_2}^2 - 2r\sigma_{M_1}\sigma_{M_2}}$$

where σ_D — standard error of the difference between the means,

σ_{M_1} — standard error of the first mean,

σ_{M_2} — standard error of the second mean,

r — coefficient of correlation between the two sets of data.

When $r = 0$, the formula assumes the familiar form of $\sigma_D = \sqrt{\sigma_{M_1}^2 + \sigma_{M_2}^2}$.

Consider a numerical example. A test has been administered to the same group of subjects on two occasions. Is there a statistically significant difference between the two average scores? The data are as follows. Number of subjects = 101. Mean scores and standard deviations respectively $M_1 = 99.1$, $M_2 = 101.8$, $\sigma_1 = 15$, $\sigma_2 = 16$. Coefficient of correlation between test results = 0.70.

The first step consists in calculating the standard errors of the first and second means.

$$\sigma_{M_1} = \frac{\sigma_1}{\sqrt{N-1}} = \frac{15}{\sqrt{100}} = 1.5$$

$$\sigma_{M_2} = \frac{\sigma_2}{\sqrt{N-1}} = \frac{16}{\sqrt{100}} = 1.6$$

Next, the standard error of the difference between the means,

$$\sigma_D = \sqrt{1.5^2 + 1.6^2 - 2 \times 0.7 \times 1.5 \times 1.6}$$
$$= \sqrt{2.25 + 2.56 - 3.36}$$
$$= \sqrt{1.45}$$
$$= 1.2$$

Hence, $t = \dfrac{101.8 - 99.1}{1.2} = \dfrac{2.7}{1.2} = 2.25$.

If small-sample methods are used, the number of degrees of freedom to be considered is given by the number of pairs compared minus one, $N - 1$. In our case, therefore, $df = 100$. Thus we see that the t-ratio of 2·25 indicates significance at the 5 per cent level of confidence but not at the 1 per cent level. If the coefficient of correlation had not been taken into account in the computation of the standard error, we would have found the difference between the means not significant at the 5 per cent level when, in fact, it is significant.

CHAPTER X

Correlation Methods

The product-moment method of calculating the coefficient of correlation, discussed in the last chapter, must be regarded as the fundamental and the strict one. In the present chapter we shall deal with several other methods which, although open to certain criticisms and subject to various limitations, are very useful when not all or when none of the sets of correlated data are given in the form of frequency distributions of measures.

Biserial Correlation. The biserial coefficient, r_{bi}, is used to measure the degree of correlation between two variables when one is given in the form of a frequency distribution and the other is in the form of a dichotomous (or, twofold) classification; the latter may be exemplified by such classifications as those of men into tall and short or of pupils into the ones who passed and the ones who failed to pass an examination.

The formula for the biserial coefficient of correlation given later is very useful, even though it has been developed on certain assumptions regarding the nature of the data. Thus, before applying the formula it is clearly necessary to be satisfied that the particular set of data can be justifiably used.

The only assumption regarding the frequency distribution is that it is obtained from a sample which is representative of the parent population, and that its standard deviation is a good estimate of the parametric standard deviation. We have already seen that for fairly large samples it is reasonable to accept that the sample sigma is the same as the parametric population sigma.

With regard to the dichotomous classification the assumption made is much more stringent. It is that underlying the classification is a normal distribution of a continuous variable, and that the classification merely divides the normally distributed individuals into those above and those below a certain value of the variable quality. Suppose that this quality is the knowledge of arithmetic. If a group of children are tested for their knowledge of this subject, each child will show some knowledge, and this will be represented by the child's test score or examination mark. The test scores and even the knowledge of arithmetic which they represent may be not unreasonably assumed to be normally distributed. Then, scores above a certain value may be regarded as passes and below that value as failures. Provided our twofold classification is obtained, or may be assumed to be obtained, on such a basis, the condition regarding the classification is satisfied.

The dichotomous classification divides the continuously distributed variable into two groups. For instance, if we were to measure the correlation between the results of an intelligence test and those of a scholarship examination, then the test scores could be divided into two groups of (a) the scores of those children who passed the examination, and (b) those who failed to pass it. Now if

M_p is the higher mean of obtained scores from one of the groups,

M_q — the lower mean (i.e., the mean of the other group),

p — the proportion of the cases in the higher group,

q — the proportion of the cases in the lower group,

σ_t — the standard deviation of the total distribution of the continuous variable,

y — the height of the ordinate which divides the normal curve of unit area into two segments in the proportion $p : q$,

then the coefficient of biserial correlation is given by

$$r_{bi} = \frac{M_p - M_q}{\sigma_t} \times \frac{pq}{y}$$

An alternative form of the formula is

$$r_{bi} = \frac{M_p - M_t}{\sigma_t} \times \frac{p}{y}$$

where M_t is the mean of the total distribution of the continuous variable. This form is more convenient when a number of biserial coefficients have to be calculated between the same continuously distributed variable and several dichotomous classifications. Such a situation may arise, for example, in mental testing, when test items of the right-wrong type are correlated with total test scores.

Consider the following example. Suppose we have the results of an "intelligence test" of our own construction for 200 children, and we know also which of these children have passed a scholarship examination and which have failed, but have no further information about marks or order of merit. We may then calculate the biserial correlation coefficient between our test and the scholarship examination results. The data and calculation are set out in Table XL.

TABLE XL

BISERIAL CORRELATION BETWEEN TEST SCORES AND EXAMINATION RESULTS

Col. 1	Col. 2	Col. 3	Col. 4	Col. 5	Col. 6	Col. 7	Col. 8	Col. 9	Col. 10
Test Scores	Number of Examination Passes f_p	Number of Examination Failures f_q	Deviations from A.M. x	x^2	$f_p x$	$f_q x$	f_t $(f_p + f_q)$	$f_t x$	$f_t x^2$
90–99	4	0	4	16	16	0	4	16	64
80–89	7	0	3	9	21	0	7	21	63
70–79	21	2	2	4	42	4	23	46	92
60–69	24	11	1	1	24	11	35	35	35
50–59	31	18	—	—	—	—	49	—	—
40–49	23	23	−1	1	−23	−23	46	−46	46
30–39	8	11	−2	4	−16	−22	19	−38	76
20–29	2	6	−3	9	−6	−18	8	−24	72
10–19	0	6	−4	16	0	−24	6	−24	96
0–9	0	3	−5	25	0	−15	3	−15	75
	120	80			+58	−87	200	−29	619

Assumed Mean $= 54.5$

$$M_p = 54.5 + \frac{58}{120} \times 10 = 59.3$$

$$M_q = 54.5 - \frac{87}{80} \times 10 = 43.6$$

$$p = \frac{120}{200} = 0.60$$

$$q = \frac{80}{200} = 0.40$$

$$\sigma_t = 10 \sqrt{\frac{639}{200} - \left(\frac{-29}{200}\right)^2} = 17.52$$

$$y = 0.386 \text{ from Table XLI below}$$

$$r_{bi} = \frac{59.3 - 43.6}{17.46} \times \frac{0.60 \times 0.40}{0.386}$$

$$\therefore r_{bi} = 0.556$$

The steps in the calculation are as follows:

1. M_p and M_q are calculated by the short method from an assumed mean. The latter is taken midway in class interval 50–59, being therefore equal to 54.5.

$\Sigma f_p x$ is entered at the foot of Column 6 and is $+58$; $\Sigma f_q x$, at the foot of Column 7, is -87. Since $M = AM + \frac{\Sigma f x}{N} i$, as explained in Chapter II, $M_p = 59.3$ and $M_q = 43.6$, as shown in the calculation immediately below Table XL.

2. By definition $p =$ proportion of cases in higher group; $\therefore p = \frac{120}{200} = 0.6$; similarly $q = 0.4$.

3. The standard deviation of the total distribution is obtained by the short method, as explained in Chapter III. Squared deviations from the assumed mean are set out in Column 5, and fx^2 values in Column 10.

We have seen that in general $\sigma = i\sqrt{\dfrac{\Sigma f x'^2}{N} - c'^2}$. In our example, deviations from assumed mean are denoted by x. $\Sigma f_t x^2 = 619$, entered at the foot of Column 10. Hence

$$\sigma_t = 10\sqrt{\frac{639}{200} - \left(\frac{-29}{200}\right)^2} \text{ (as shown below the table),}$$

giving $\sigma_t = 17\cdot52$.

4. The value of y, the ordinate which divides a normal curve of unit area into two segments in the proportion of $0\cdot6:0\cdot4$ may, of course, be calculated from known normal distribution constants; but it is most conveniently obtained from a table, such as Table XLI.

TABLE XLI

ORDINATES (y) CORRESPONDING TO POINTS OF DIVISION OF THE AREA UNDER THE NORMAL CURVE INTO A LARGER PROPORTION (A) AND A SMALLER PROPORTION (B)

A	0·50	0·55	0·60	0·65	0·70	0·75	0·80	0·85	0·90	0·95
B	0·50	0·45	0·40	0·35	0·30	0·25	0·20	0·15	0·10	0·05
y	0·399	0·396	0·386	0·370	0·348	0·318	0·280	0·233	0·176	0·103

The Reliability of the Biserial Correlation Coefficient. Like any other statistic, r_{bi} values should be examined for reliability. To do this, it is necessary to calculate confidence limits for some acceptable confidence level. Confidence limits of a statistic depend on its standard error.

The standard error of a biserial coefficient of correlation is given by

$$\sigma r_{bi} = \frac{\frac{\sqrt{pq}}{y} - r_{bi}{}^2}{\sqrt{N}}$$

We may now calculate the standard error of the correlation between test scores and examination results of our last example. In this case: $p = 0\cdot6, q = 0\cdot4, y = 0\cdot386, N = 200$ and $r_{bi} = 0\cdot556$. Substituting these values into the formula we have

$$\sigma r_{bi} = \frac{\frac{\sqrt{0\cdot6 \times 0\cdot4}}{0\cdot386} - (0\cdot556)^2}{\sqrt{200}}$$

$$= 0\cdot067$$

The larger our sample the more are we justified in regarding the sampling distribution as normal; for small samples t-distributions appropriate to the sample size must be used for computing confidence limits. Here, at the 1 per cent level of confidence $r_{bi} = 0.556 \pm 2.6 \times 0.068$, i.e., r_{bi} lies between 0.379 and 0.733. We must, therefore, conclude that there is a fairly high statistically significant correlation between "intelligence" test scores and examination passes and failures for our group of children.

Fourfold or Tetrachoric Correlation. When the data are available in the form of a 2×2 contingency table, and a measure of correlation between the two variables is required, then in certain circumstances the tetrachoric correlation coefficient, r_t, may be computed.

Suppose that instead of a correlation between test scores and examination results, a correlation between examination results in two subjects is to be calculated. The only information available is whether a child has passed or failed to pass in each subject, say, English and Arithmetic.

Now the special circumstances under which the r_t formula given below may be used must be fully appreciated. It is necessary to assume that the two dichotomous classifications have at the back of them two continuous normal distributions; then, at some value of one variable and at another value of the other variable the distributions are divided up into two groups each.

Thus, examination marks may be arranged to be normally distributed. Then, scores above a certain mark are passes and below that mark are failures. In this way a set of 100 examination results in English and Arithmetic may be fitted into a 2×2 table, such as Table XLII.

Two variables classified in this manner may be correlated by more than one method. No very simple computation of the correlation coefficient is possible. Quite a good approximation to the true r_t may be obtained from the following equation:

$$\frac{ad - bc}{N^2 yy'} = r_t + \frac{zz'}{2} r_t^2 \text{ (approx.)}$$

where (1) a, b, c and d are numbers in cells a, b, c and d respectively (see Table XLII),

(2) N is the total number of cases,

(3) y and y' are respectively the heights of the ordinates which divide normal curves of unit area into segments in the proportions of $p:q$ and $p':q'$, and

(4) z and z' are respectively the standard scores of normal curves of unit area where they are divided into the segments, as indicated above.

TABLE XLII

FOURFOLD CLASSIFICATION OF EXAMINATION RESULTS
IN ENGLISH AND ARITHMETIC

ENGLISH
Pass   Failure

	Pass	Failure	
ARITHMETIC Pass	a 50	b 10	$p = 0.6$
			$y = 0.386$
Failure	c 20	d 20	$q = 0.4$

$p' = 0.7$ $q' = 0.3$
$y' = 0.348$

It is clear that the computational work involved will necessarily be quite considerable. Very simple artificial data are therefore used to illustrate the procedure.

To calculate the tetrachoric coefficient of correlation between the examination results in English and Arithmetic, as set out in Table XLII, we may work step-by-step in the following way:

1. From the given values of a, b, c and d we see that the total number of passes in Arithmetic is 60 and the number of failures is 40. Therefore, $p = \dfrac{60}{100} = 0.6$, and $q = \dfrac{40}{100} = 0.4$.

Similarly, since the total number of passes in English is 70 and the number of failures is 30, $p' = \dfrac{70}{100} = 0.7$ and $q' = \dfrac{30}{100} = 0.3$.

2. From Table XLI we note that the y-value corresponding

to $p = 0.6$ and $q = 0.4$ is 0.386; the y'-value corresponding to $p' = 0.7$ and $q' = 0.3$ is 0.348.

3. z-values could, of course, be calculated from known normal distribution constants, but they may be conveniently obtained from tables, such as Table XLIII below.

TABLE XLIII

STANDARD SCORES (z) CORRESPONDING TO POINTS OF DIVISION OF THE AREAS UNDER THE NORMAL CURVE INTO A LARGER PROPORTION (A), AND A SMALLER PROPORTION (B)

A	0·50	0·55	0·60	0·65	0·70	0·75	0·80	0·85	0·vo	0·95
B	0·50	0·45	0·40	0·35	0·30	0·25	0·20	0·15	0·10	0·05
z	0	0·126	0·253	0·385	0·524	0·675	0·842	1·04	1·28	1·64

From Table XLIII we note that the z-value corresponding to $p = 0.6$ and $q = 0.4$ is 0.253; the z'-value corresponding to $p' = 0.7$ and $q' = 0.3$ is 0.524.

4. We may now substitute the various values into our equation. Thus we have

$$\frac{50 \times 20 - 10 \times 20}{100^2 \times 0.386 \times 0.348} = r_t + \frac{0.253 \times 0.524}{2} r_t^2$$

$$\text{or } 0.595 = r_t + 0.066\, r_t^2 \text{ (approx.)}$$

Rearranging terms:

$$0.066\, r_t^2 + r_t - 0.595 = 0$$

This is a simple quadratic equation of the standard form

$$ax^2 + bx + c = 0$$

whose solution is

$$x_{1,\, 2} = \frac{-b \pm \sqrt{b^2 - 4ac}}{2a}$$

Solving for r_t we have

$$r_t = \frac{-1 \pm \sqrt{1^2 - 4 \times 0.066 \times (-0.595)}}{2 \times 0.066}$$

Only the positive root leads here to a meaningful value of a coefficient of correlation. We see that

$$r_t = \frac{-1 + \sqrt{1 + 4 \times 0\cdot066 \times 0\cdot595}}{2 \times 0\cdot066}$$

whence $r_t = 0\cdot57$ (approx. only)

Though not difficult, this direct procedure of calculating the tetrachoric coefficient of correlation is tedious and time-consuming; this is the case even with artificial, simple data such as ours, and when only three decimal places resulting in considerable inaccuracies are used. Thurstone and others have prepared the so-called Computing Diagrams for the Tetrachoric Correlation Coefficient; with their help the computational work may be greatly simplified.

Finally it should be noted that contingency tables such as those used in tetrachoric correlation are also amenable to a χ^2-test of a null hypothesis asserting no relationship between the two variables. Certain corrections, however, which have not been described in this book, must be used for 2×2 contingency tables (i.e., one degree of freedom). In fact, it might be simplest to ascertain first by means of a χ^2-test whether there is reason to believe that a significant correlation exists between the two variables. If this is so, then we may proceed to measure the correlation by computing r_t. The reliability of the obtained value of the coefficient may be ascertained by computing its standard error in the usual manner. The formula is not a simple one, and the treatment is beyond the scope of this book. We must now concern ourselves with certain other important correlation methods.

Correlating Rankings. We have seen that when a pair of variables can be expressed as measurements or scores and when in a series of cases the values for the pair are given, then the correlation between the variables can be established by the Pearson-Bravais product-moment method. Not infrequently however, the variables cannot be stated precisely enough to be capable of quantification. And yet, such variables as, for example, human preferences, judgements, or attitudes, though not easily quantifiable, may manifestly correlate with one another to a greater or lesser extent.

Although not strictly measurable, the things or persons to be judged may simply be arranged in order, either according to some quality which they all possess to a varying degree or, perhaps, in order of preference where no objective quality is involved. Such an order is called *a ranking* because each member in it has a rank. Correlations between rankings may then be established by means of the so-called *rank correlation formulae*.

Ranking in order of merit and correlating rankings have found many applications in various fields of the social sciences. Among others, these methods have been used in inquiries into social attitudes, in investigations of the effectiveness of advertisements, in studies of personality traits, in inquiries into aesthetic preferences, in personnel selection and allocation work, etc., etc.

With measurable variables perfect positive correlation is conventionally $+1$ and perfect negative correlation is -1. This arrangement is adhered to in rank correlation work. As will be seen presently, there are a number of different rank correlation formulae in use. However, in each case a perfect positive correlation will work out to be $+1$ and a perfect inverse correlation -1.

When a correlation is not perfect, then the numerical values of the correlation coefficients obtained for a given pair of rankings by the different formulae will not be the same. This need not give rise to difficulty in practice. We may regard correlation as measured by the different formulae to be given by reference to different scales.

Kendall's τ (tau) Rank Correlation Coefficient.
Kendall's correlation coefficient τ (tau) is given by:

$$\tau = \frac{P - Q}{\frac{1}{2}n(n - 1)}$$

where n is the number of items per ranking,

P — the positive score (in second ranking), and

Q — the negative score (in second ranking).

We must now see what, precisely, P and Q stand for. This is best explained by reference to a numerical example.

Suppose that 12 men in a workshop are ranked in order of merit regarding, say, their dependability by their foreman and their charge-hand, as shown in Table XLIV.

What measure of agreement is there between the foreman and the charge-hand, or what is the correlation between their judgements?

First, we may re-arrange one of the rankings, say, the foreman's, and set it out in the natural order, as shown in Table
XLV.

TABLE XLIV

ORDER OF MERIT RANKINGS OF TWELVE MEN

Man	A	B	C	D	E	F	G	H	J	K	L	M
Rank given by Foreman	6	5	11	1	12	3	2	7	10	8	4	9
Rank given by Charge-hand	5	3	10	4	9	6	2	7	12	11	1	8

TABLE XLV

ORDER OF MERIT RANKINGS REARRANGED

Man	D	G	F	L	B	A	H	K	M	J	C	E
Rank by Foreman	1	2	3	4	5	6	7	8	9	10	11	12
Rank by Charge-hand	4	2	6	1	3	5	7	11	8	12	10	9

We may arbitrarily call the foreman's the first ranking. We
might have, of course, arranged the charge-hand's ranking in
its natural order and regard it as the first ranking. This would
not have affected our final result.

Now, as the table stands, the charge-hand's ranking is the
second. Let us see what are the P and Q values obtained from
it. Consider the first man, D; he is ranked fourth in the
second ranking. In front of him are "correctly" placed the
following: F, A, H, K, M, J, C and E, that is 8 towards the
total positive score. Consider the second man, G; those
placed "correctly" in front of him are: F, B, A, H, K, M, J,
C and E (but not L), that is another 9 towards the total
positive score.

In this manner we may obtain the total positive score in
the second ranking. It is made up as follows:

D—8	B—7	M—3
G—9	A—6	J—0
F—6	H—5	C—0
L—8	K—1	E—0

This gives a total of $P = 53$.

Similarly we may find the value of Q. Consider the first man, D; in front of him the following are "incorrectly" placed: G, L and B, that is 3 towards the total negative score. In this way the total negative score is obtained as follows:

D—3	B—0	M—0
G—1	A—0	J—2
F—3	H—0	C—1
L—0	K—3	E—0

This gives a total of $Q = 13$.

Now 12 men were ranked, and therefore, n, the number of items per ranking, is 12. Hence

$$\tau = (53 - 13)/[\tfrac{1}{2} \times 12(12 - 1)]$$
$$= 40/(6 \times 11) = 0.606 \text{ (approx.)}$$

Consider again the τ formula, $\tau = \dfrac{P - Q}{\tfrac{1}{2}n(n - 1)}$. The numerator gives the difference between the positive and negative scores (in second ranking). Now the total number of comparisons which can be made is given by the denominator, $\tfrac{1}{2}n(n - 1)$ [which equals the number of ways of choosing two things from n]. This equals the maximum value of the score (in second ranking); and the maximum value is attained when the second ranking is the same as the first. The maximum score is also given by $(P + Q)$, which, clearly, is the total number of comparisons which can be made. Thus,

$$\tfrac{1}{2}n(n - 1) = P + Q$$

We may, therefore, write

$$\tau = (P - Q)/(P + Q)$$

Denoting $(P + Q)$ by T, we have $Q = T - P$. Therefore,

$$\tau = [P - (T - P)]/T$$
$$\text{or } \tau = (2P - T)/T$$

which is another useful form of the τ formula.

It may be noted that T depends only on the number of items per rank. It need not even be remembered that it equals $\frac{1}{2}n(n - 1)$, because it is the maximum score obtainable, i.e., the score when the two rankings are identical. In the last example, if the charge-hand's ranking had been the same as the foreman's, T would have been obtained from: 11 for D plus 10 for G plus 9 for F, etc.; thus T would have been given by $11 + 10 + 9 + 8 + 7 + 6 + 5 + 4 + 3 + 2 + 1 = 66$. Since P in the example is 53,

$$\tau = [(2 \times 53) - 66]/66 = 40/66 = 0\cdot606, \text{ as before.}$$

The tau rank correlations formula may, of course, be used for rankings of any length. It should be noted, however, that it lends itself particularly conveniently to being used with shorter rankings (containing, say, up to 20 items).

Sometimes in practice two or more individuals are given the same rank. If this occurs in a ranking, then the two or more members are said to be tied. If the τ formula is used to obtain a measure of correlation between two rankings in one or both of which some members are tied, certain complications arise. Two correlation procedures are then open. It may be argued that each is useful in certain special circumstances. It is advisable to avoid tied ranks whenever possible. If there is no escape, the advanced student may consult M. G. Kendall's *Rank Correlation Methods*.

Spearman's ρ (rho) Rank Correlation Coefficient. Spearman's correlation coefficient ρ is given by

$$\rho = 1 - \frac{6\Sigma(d^2)}{n_3 - n}$$

where n is the number of items per ranking (as before), and
       d — the difference in rank of items in a pair.
The rho rank correlation formula is most useful with longer rankings.

Suppose that 30 pictures are ranked in order of preference by two judges. Having ranked the pictures from the most down to the least beautiful, the first judge labels them 1, 2, 3, 4, and so on down to 30. The second judge then ranks the 30 pictures, and the two rankings may be ranged side by side, as shown in Table XLVI.

TABLE XLVI

RANKED PREFERENCES OF THIRTY PICTURES BY TWO JUDGES

nking by Judge No. 1	1	2	3	4	5	6	7	8	9	10	11	12	13	14	15
nking by Judge No. 2	2	4	3	1	5	7	10	17	8	9	14	6	15	11	13
fference in rank (d)	1	2	0	3	0	1	3	9	1	1	3	6	2	3	2
d^2	1	4	0	9	0	1	9	81	1	1	9	36	4	9	4

nking by Judge No. 1	16	17	18	19	20	21	22	23	24	25	26	27	28	29	30	
nking by Judge No. 2	12	18	19	21	16	23	30	29	20	22	25	24	28	26	27	
fference in rank (d)	4	1	1	2	4	2	8	6	4	3	1	3	0	3	3	Total
d^2	16	1	1	4	16	4	64	36	16	9	1	9	0	9	9	364

Rank order differences are then listed underneath each pair of ranks, and finally in the bottom row there are the d^2-values. The sum of the latter, $\Sigma(d^2)$ is 364.

Substituting our numerical values into the ρ formula, we have:

$$1 - \frac{6 \times 364}{30(30^2 - 1)}$$

$$\therefore \rho = 0.918$$

Spearman's Footrule Formula for Rank Correlation. Sometimes another formula for rank correlation, known as Spearman's Footrule or R coefficient is used. It will be seen that it has several disadvantages, but it is simple and quick to use. The Footrule coefficient of correlation is given by

$$R = 1 - \frac{6\Sigma g}{n^2 - 1}$$

where n is the number of items per ranking (as before), and g — the gain in rank of second ranking items with respect to the first ranking items (considered in each pair).

It may be noted that R is much less sensitive than either τ or ρ. Thus, the same change in the order of members of one of the two rankings may result in a smaller change in the R-value than in either the τ- or the ρ-values.

The R-formula must be regarded as a simplification of the ρ-formula. Using the latter as a criterion, the correlation measures given by R are correct only when $R = +1$ or $R = -1$. At other values of R it is necessary to correct the result. The corrected value of correlation, denoted by r, is given by

$$r = \sin \frac{\pi}{2} R$$

There is another important limitation to the use of the Footrule formula. It is that the formula can only be used for positive correlation. If a negative result is obtained, one of the rankings must be reversed; then, the sign of the R-value obtained in this manner is also reversed. This is the only legitimate procedure of computing a negative correlation by the Footrule method.

It may further be pointed out that the scales of measurement of rank correlation based on the tau and rho methods are symmetrical about the zero values. Thus, corresponding to any given positive value of τ and of ρ, there is a negative value of the same magnitude arising from an inversion of one of the rankings. This is not the case with R-values obtained from the Footrule formula.

By way of a numerical example, let us use the Footrule formula in conjunction with the data of Table XLVI. The two rankings and the "gains in rank" are set out in Table XLVII.

We see that only gains in rank, or positive rank differences, are considered; negative rank differences are no gains and are, therefore, ignored. The sum of the gains, Σg, is 41. Substituting numerical values into the formula, we have

$$R = 1 - \frac{6 \times 41}{30^2 - 1}$$

$$\therefore R = 0 \cdot 725$$

TABLE XLVII

RANKED PREFERENCES OF THIRTY PICTURES BY TWO JUDGES

RANKING (1)	1	2	3	4	5	6	7	8	9	10	
Ranking (2)	2	4	3	1	5	7	10	17	8	9	
Gain in Rank	1	2	—	—	—	1	3	9	—	—	
Ranking (1)	11	12	13	14	15	16	17	18	19	20	
Ranking (2)	14	6	15	11	13	12	18	19	21	16	
Gain in Rank	3	—	2	—	—	—	1	1	2	—	
Ranking (1)	21	22	23	24	25	26	27	28	29	30	
Ranking (2)	23	30	29	20	22	25	24	28	26	27	Total
Gain in Rank	2	8	6	—	—	—	—	—	—	—	41

This value is considerably lower than the one obtained by the ρ-formula. It may, however, be corrected. Thus,

$$r = \sin \frac{\pi}{2}(0 \cdot 725)$$
$$= \sin (0 \cdot 725 \times 90°)$$
$$= \sin 65 \cdot 25° \ (\text{or} \ \sin 65° \ 15')$$

From tables of natural sines we find that
$$r = 0 \cdot 908$$

We see that this result is now quite close to that obtained earlier by the rho formula ($\rho = 0 \cdot 918$). It will be appreciated that when rankings are long and the differences in rank large, then the arithmetic may be considerably simplified if the Footrule formula (preferably corrected) is used.

CHAPTER XI

The Analysis of Variance

The statistical significance of a difference between two means was discussed in earlier chapters. What if there are more than two means to compare? Not infrequently one is confronted with several groups, wondering whether they may all be regarded as samples of the same population, or alternatively whether the groups differ so considerably from one another that the null hypothesis of a common parent population behind all the groups must be rejected.

If there are only a few groups then it is a relatively simple matter to compare their means pair by pair; in each case the critical ratio of t-test is used. When there are three groups of measurements, three such tests will be necessary. When there are four groups: A, B, C and D, the following six comparisons will have to be made: $A - B$, $A - C$, $A - D$, $B - C$, $B - D$ and $C - D$. When there are ten groups as many as forty-five tests will have to be carried out. Clearly, at this rate the task of comparing means pair by pair soon becomes prodigious. The analysis of variance, in its simplest form, is a more rapid means of testing the null hypothesis that several groups derive from a common population. Instead of considering groups pair by pair, the analysis of variance considers all the groups together and submits them to an overall test. It will be noted, however, that this overall test still has to be sometimes followed by a few individual t-tests.

In its simplest form the analysis of variance may thus be regarded as an extension or a development of the t-test. In this chapter we shall concern ourselves with this function of the analysis of variance. It must not be thought, however, that this covers its full field of application. On the contrary, the technique of the analysis of variance is used extensively in statistics for various purposes. Once the basic procedures of the technique are grasped, the more advanced student will have little difficulty in applying the analysis of variance to a wide range of problems.

Two Estimates of Variance. The variance of a distribution is one of the measures of its scatter. It is equal to the square of the standard deviation. It is simply denoted by σ^2. For any particular distribution,

$$\sigma^2 = \frac{\Sigma x^2}{N}$$

where x — the deviation of a measurement from the mean of the distribution,

N — the number of cases in the distribution.

The null hypothesis of the analysis of variance asserts that the several groups are all samples drawn from a common parent population. In order to test this hypothesis two independent estimates of the population variance are made. If the two estimates give widely different results, the hypothesis is falsified.

One of the estimates of the population variance is based on the variation of the measurements within the several groups. The other estimate is based on the variation between the group means. Now if the groups are all alike, these two estimates of variance will be alike. But if the variations between groups are considerably greater than those within them, then the groups are probably not samples of the same population; in fact, they probably represent different parent populations.

The Test of Statistical Significance. The estimate of the population variance that is based on the variation between groups is known as the *mean square between groups*. The estimate of the population variance that is based on the variation within groups is known as the *mean square within groups*. The so-called variance ratio, denoted by F, is given by:

$$F = \frac{\text{Mean square between groups}}{\text{Mean square within groups}}$$

If the actual calculated variance ratio turns out to be greater than the F-values corresponding to the generally accepted levels of statistical significance (commonly the 5 per cent and the 1 per cent levels) in standard tables for the distribution of F, then the groups cannot be considered as differing from one another merely as a result of sampling error. Thus the F-test is a test of statistical significance of the differences among the several groups, just as the t-test is a test of statistical significance of the difference between two groups.

The Calculation of the Sum of Squares. The first step towards the determination of the mean squares between and within groups is the calculation of three sums of squares: (a) the total sum of squares, (b) the sum of squares between groups, and (c) the sum of squares within groups.

Let us assume that there are a groups, and n cases in each group. Let N be the total number of cases. Then, obviously, $N = a \times n$.

(a) The total sum of squares is by definition given by Σx^2. If we deal with raw measurements, X, instead of deviations, x, then

$$\text{the total sum of squares} = \Sigma X^2 - \frac{(\Sigma X)^2}{N}$$

The student may note the derivation of this expression. If X denotes the mean, then

$$
\begin{aligned}
x &= X - \overline{X} \\
\therefore \quad x^2 &= (X - \overline{X})^2 \\
&= X^2 - 2X\overline{X} + \overline{X}^2 \\
\text{Hence,} \quad \Sigma x^2 &= \Sigma X^2 - 2\overline{X}\Sigma X + N\overline{X}^2
\end{aligned}
$$

$$\text{Since } \overline{X} = \frac{\Sigma X}{N}, \ \Sigma X = N\overline{X}$$

Substituting this into the expression for Σx^2,

$$
\begin{aligned}
\Sigma x^2 &= \Sigma X^2 - 2N\overline{X}^2 + N\overline{X}^2 \\
&= \Sigma X^2 - N\overline{X}^2 \\
&= \Sigma X^2 - \frac{N(\Sigma X)^2}{N^2} \\
&= \Sigma X^2 - \frac{(\Sigma X)^2}{N}
\end{aligned}
$$

(b) The sum of squares between groups is given by

$$\frac{(\Sigma X_1)^2}{n} + \frac{(\Sigma X_2)^2}{n} + \frac{(\Sigma X_3)^2}{n} + \ldots - \frac{(\Sigma X)^2}{N}$$

where X_1, X_2, X_3, etc., denote raw measurements in the 1st, 2nd, 3rd, etc., groups respectively.

In the general expression for the sum of squares between groups the various expressions are not brought to a common denominator because when groups are of unequal size it is necessary to add appropriate suffixes to n-values, which then become n_1, n_2, n_3, etc.

(c) The sum of squares within groups is given by the difference between the total sum of squares and the sum of squares between groups. This is the quickest way of calculating it. A direct calculation may be used as a check.

To calculate directly the sum of squares within groups, we must obtain first the sum of squares within each group. Then the sum of these expressions gives the value of the sum of squares within groups.

The Calculation of the Mean Squares. The mean squares necessary for the calculation of the F-ratio are obtained by dividing the sums of squares between and within groups by appropriate values of degrees of freedom.

The total number of degrees of freedom is $(N - 1)$. The number of degrees of freedom between a groups is $(a - 1)$. The number of degrees of freedom by which to divide the sum of squares within groups is $a(n - 1)$, which equals $(an - a)$ or $(N - a)$.

Thus:

$$\text{Mean square between groups} = \frac{\text{Sum of squares between groups}}{a - 1}$$

$$\text{Mean square within groups} = \frac{\text{Sum of squares within groups}}{N - a}$$

It should be noted that the total number of degrees of freedom equals the sum of df between groups and df within groups:

$$N - 1 = (a - 1) + (N - a)$$

Likewise, as mentioned earlier, the total sum of squares equals *the sum* of the sum of squares between groups and the sum of squares within groups.

Some Assumptions. Two major assumptions are made about a set of data that is submitted to the analysis of variance. To start with, it is assumed that the distribution of cases within each group is normal. Therefore, if the distributions of measurements depart very considerably from normality, the analysis of variance should not be used.

Then, it is assumed that the cases within every one of the groups are scattered equally, that is, that the variances within the groups are the same. The homogeneity of variance, as it is known, may be checked. This is done by Bartlett's test of the homogeneity of variance which involves the use of chi-squared. A modification of it is sometimes referred to as the Hartley test. A crude check may be made by dividing each of the separate sums of squares within the several groups by the corresponding *df*-value to see if the thus obtained variances are in fact all reasonably alike.

The *F*-Test and the *t*-Test. If the analysis of variance results in a sufficiently small value of *F* we conclude that the null hypothesis is upheld, that is, that it may be assumed that the samples have been drawn at random from a common parent population. But it does not follow that if we compared two samples characterised by extreme means, say, the largest and the smallest of all, then they would turn out not to be significantly different. The means of two such groups could indeed prove to be significantly different because these two samples have not been taken at random but have, in fact, been deliberately selected.

If the *F*-test indicates significance, that is, that the samples cannot be assumed to have been drawn from a common parent population, then the various individual means may have to be compared to carry further the investigation of the data. Selected *t*-tests must now be applied. And certain methods have been proposed as to how to go about the selection of the *t*-tests to draw as many conclusions as possible about the differences among the groups.

When there are several groups we start off the investigation of the significance of the differences among the means by using the analysis of variance. When there are only two groups we may still, if we like, use the analysis of variance instead of the *t*-test. Neither procedure has any particular advantage over the other. And in fact, as one would expect, the two procedures are mathematically equivalent. In the case of two groups $F = t^2$, or $t = \sqrt{F}$. Either a *t*-table or an *F*-table may be looked up to determine the statistical significance of the difference between two means.

A Numerical Example. Data from three samples of unequal size are set out in Table XLVIII below. May it be assumed that the samples have been drawn at random from a common population?

TABLE XLVIII

DISTRIBUTION OF MEASUREMENTS IN THREE SAMPLES

X_1		X_2			X_3		
14	15	10	10	11	17	13	12
18	15	11	12 $n_2 = 21$		15	15	14
16	13	11	15		13	13	13
13	14	14	12		15	16	13
16	13	14	13		14	16	12
14	16	12	13		15	9	13
17	12	10	7		9	10	14
15	16	9	12		8	11 $n_3 = 27$	
17 $n_1 = 18$		12	13		11	12	
15		8	13		14	12	
$\Sigma X_1 = 269$		$\Sigma X_2 = 242$			$\Sigma X_3 = 349$		
$\bar{X}_1 = \dfrac{269}{18}$ $= 14{\cdot}94$		$\bar{X}_2 = \dfrac{242}{21} = 11{\cdot}52$			$\bar{X}_3 = \dfrac{349}{27} = 12{\cdot}93$		

$\Sigma X = 860 \qquad N = 66$

The sums and averages for each group are set out immediately below the data. The next table, Table XLIX, sets out the squares of the measurements in our three groups. Directly underneath this table are given the sums of the squares.

TABLE XLIX
SQUARES OF MEASUREMENTS IN THREE SAMPLES

X_1^2		X_2^2			X_3^2		
196	225	100	100	121	289	169	144
324	225	121	144		225	225	196
256	169	121	225		169	169	169
169	196	196	144		225	256	169
256	169	196	169		196	256	144
196	256	144	169		225	81	169
289	144	100	49		81	100	196
225	256	81	144		64	121	
289		144	169		121	144	
225		64	169		196	144	
$\Sigma X_1^2 = 4{,}065$		$\Sigma X_2^2 = 2{,}870$			$\Sigma X_3^2 = 4{,}643$		

$\Sigma X^2 = 11{,}578$

Sum of squares between groups:

$$\frac{(\Sigma X_1)^2}{n_1} + \frac{(\Sigma X_2)^2}{n_2} + \frac{(\Sigma X_3)^2}{n_3} - \frac{(\Sigma X)^2}{N}$$

$$= \frac{269^2}{18} + \frac{242^2}{21} + \frac{349^2}{27} - \frac{860^2}{66}$$

$$= 4{,}020 + 2{,}789 + 4{,}511 - 11{,}206 = 114.$$

Sum of squares within groups
= Total sum of squares – Sum of squares between groups.

Total sum of squares:

$$\Sigma X^2 - \frac{(\Sigma X)^2}{N}$$

$$= 11{,}578 - \frac{860^2}{66} = 372.$$

Hence, sum of squares within groups is
$$372 - 114 = 258$$
Degrees of freedom between groups $= a - 1 = 3 - 1 = 2$.
Degrees of freedom within groups $= N - a = 66 - 3 = 63$.

We may now summarise the results as shown in Table L below.

TABLE L

ANALYSIS OF VARIANCE OF DATA IN THREE SAMPLES

Source of Variation	Sum of Squares	Degrees of Freedom	Mean Square
Between Groups	114	2	$\dfrac{114}{2} = 57 \cdot 0$
Within Groups	258	63	$\dfrac{258}{63} = 4 \cdot 095$
Total	372	65	

$$F = \frac{\text{Mean square between groups}}{\text{Mean square within groups}}$$
$$= \frac{57 \cdot 0}{4 \cdot 095} = 13 \cdot 92.$$

The last stage of the analysis consists of looking up the variance ratio tables. Table LI sets out the 5 per cent points for the distribution of F; Table LII sets out the 1 per cent points. The top row of each table gives the degrees of freedom for the greater mean square; in the case of our simple analysis variance this is the mean square between groups. The first column gives the degrees of freedom for the mean square representing in general the so-called error variance; in our case this is the mean square within groups. We see that we must enter the column headed 2; and the nearest row to $df = 63$ is the one headed 60. $F = 13 \cdot 92$ is much larger than the values of $3 \cdot 15$ and $4 \cdot 98$ in the 5 per cent and 1 per cent tables respectively. Therefore, the three samples are most unlikely to have been drawn randomly from a common population; i.e., the differences among the group means are statistically significant.

We have just carried out a simple analysis of variance where the variation of the variable is treated as if it were due to but a single factor. Data of this kind are obtained from the simplest experimental design, known as the single-classification design. More complex experimental designs call for more complex analyses of variance which are beyond the scope of this introductory text-book.

TABLE LI

THE 5 PER CENT POINTS FOR THE DISTRIBUTION OF F

Nb	Na — degrees of freedom for greater mean square.								
	1	2	3	4	6	8	12	24	∞
1	161·4	199·5	215·7	224·6	234·0	238·9	243·9	249·0	254·3
2	18·51	19·00	19·16	19·25	19·33	19·37	19·41	19·45	19·50
3	10·13	9·55	9·28	9·12	8·94	8·84	8·74	8·64	8·53
4	7·71	6·94	6·59	6·39	6·16	6·04	5·91	5·77	5·63
5	6·61	5·79	5·41	5·19	4·95	4·82	4·68	4·53	4·36
6	5·99	5·14	4·76	4·53	4·28	4·15	4·00	3·84	3·67
7	5·59	4·74	4·35	4·12	3·87	3·73	3·57	3·41	3·23
8	5·32	4·46	4·07	3·84	3·58	3·44	3·28	3·12	2·93
9	5·12	4·26	3·86	3·63	3·37	3·23	3·07	2·90	2·71
10	4·96	4·10	3·71	3·48	3·22	3·07	2·91	2·74	2·54
12	4·75	3·88	3·49	3·26	3·00	2·85	2·69	2·50	2·30
14	4·60	3·74	3·34	3·11	2·85	2·70	2·53	2·35	2·13
16	4·49	3·63	3·24	3·01	2·74	2·59	2·42	2·24	2·01
20	4·35	3·49	3·10	2·87	2·60	2·45	2·28	2·08	1·84
25	4·24	3·38	2·99	2·76	2·49	2·34	2·16	1·96	1·71
30	4·17	3·32	2·92	2·69	2·42	2·27	2·09	1·89	1·62
40	4·08	3·23	2·84	2·61	2·34	2·18	2·00	1·79	1·51
60	4·00	3·15	2·76	2·52	2·25	2·10	1·92	1·70	1·39
120	3·92	3·07	2·68	2·45	2·17	2·02	1·83	1·61	1·25
∞	3·84	2·99	2·60	2·37	2·09	1·94	1·75	1·52	1·00

TABLE LII

THE I PER CENT POINTS FOR THE DISTRIBUTION OF F

Nb	Na — degrees of freedom for greater mean square.								
	I	2	3	4	6	8	12	24	∞
I	4052	4999	5403	5625	5859	5981	6106	6234	6366
2	98·49	99·00	99·17	99·25	99·33	99·36	99·42	99·46	99·50
3	34·12	30·81	29·46	28·71	27·91	27·49	27·05	26·60	26·12
4	21·20	18·00	16·69	15·98	15·21	14·80	14·37	13·93	13·46
5	16·26	13·27	12·06	11·39	10·67	10·29	9·89	9·47	9·02
6	13·74	10·92	9·78	9·15	8·47	8·10	7·72	7·31	6·88
7	12·25	9·55	8·45	7·85	7·19	6·84	6·47	6·07	5·65
8	11·26	8·65	7·59	7·01	6·37	6·03	5·67	5·28	4·86
9	10·56	8·02	6·99	6·42	5·80	5·47	5·11	4·73	4·31
10	10·04	7·56	6·55	5·99	5·39	5·06	4·71	4·33	3·91
12	9·33	6·93	5·95	5·41	4·82	4·50	4·16	3·78	3·36
14	8·86	6·51	5·56	5·03	4·46	4·14	3·80	3·43	3·00
16	8·53	6·23	5·29	4·77	4·20	3·89	3·55	3·18	2·75
20	8·10	5·85	4·94	4·43	3·87	3·56	3·23	2·86	2·42
25	7·77	5·57	4·68	4·18	3·63	3·32	2·99	2·62	2·17
30	7·56	5·39	4·51	4·02	3·47	3·17	2·84	2·47	2·01
40	7·31	5·18	4·31	3·83	3·29	2·99	2·66	2·29	1·80
60	7·08	4·98	4·13	3·65	3·12	2·82	2·50	2·12	1·60
120	6·85	4·79	3·95	3·48	2·96	2·66	2·34	1·95	1·38
∞	6·64	4·60	3·78	3·32	2·80	2·51	2·18	1·79	1·00

Tables LI and LII reprinted in rearranged form from Table V of Fisher and Yates, *Statistical Tables for Biological, Agricultural and Medical Research*, Oliver and Boyd Ltd, Edinburgh, by permission of the authors and publishers.

Index